Finding Grandma:

A Sentimental Journey
Through 1920s Columbia County Recipes

Finding Grandma:

A Sentimental Journey
Through 1920s Columbia County Recipes

MARY BETH WENGER

Finding Grandma: A Sentimental Journey Through 1920s Columbia County Recipes
Copyright © 2013 by Mary Beth Wenger
Find out more at www.FINDINGGRANDMABOOK.com

Book design by Jessika Hazelton

Printed in the United States of America

The Troy Book Makers • Troy, New York • thetroybookmakers.com

To order additional copies of this title,
contact your favorite local bookstore
or visit www.tbmbooks.com

ISBN: 978-1-61468-1984

For my Mother, who told me the stories

Author's Note

This story is a mix of fact and fancy. **The stories of my family and myself are all true,** but what Grandma Edna might have thought or said during the 1920s is pure fiction. Other characters, like Mrs. Barringer, did exist (hence the many recipes named for her), but outside of knowing that she took in laundry, what she said, what she thought, what she looked like, or how many children she had is entirely a product of the author's imagination.

The recipes in italics are transcribed verbatim from the pages of my grandmother's cookbook, so please do not be put off by misspellings and unusual spellings. It was important to retain the unique character of the entries exactly as they appear.

Table Of Contents

January, 2010

On a chill Sunday in January, my 85-year-old Mother and I sat in her kitchen and gazed out the window as chunks of ice bumped into each other on the Hudson River below us, like cubes jockeying in a frosty glass of lemonade. The badgering winter wind poked its chill nose into every nook and cranny, mocking us as it whistled past the window. We bent over clutched teacups, inhaling the warming curls of steam as if they were the very elixir of life.

Suddenly, as if a cartoon light bulb had gone off atop my mother's head she blurted,

"Your grandmother's recipes! Go down to the cellar and find them! They're wrapped up in plastic, right next to the Christmas decorations!" This was said with no small degree of urgency, as if it needed to be done right here, right now, this instant.

We hadn't been talking about cooking or family. And in more than a half-century of being her child, I had never once heard my Mother mention having possession of her own mother's recipe book. That wasn't entirely surprising, because my grandmother, Edna Coons Yager, died when my own Mother was merely 5 years old. Outside of having made my own mental inventory of handed-down family jewelry, flower urns, quilts and the like, it had never occurred to me to wonder if any culinary artifacts from my mother's childhood had survived. All of that seemed— and was—so long ago. And while my Mother tells me that I strongly resemble my grandmother physically, ("especially around the eyes," she opines) that seemed to be the end of the connection, since I never actually met my Grandma. Mainly, what I had discerned from family lore was that Fate had been cruel to Grandma Edna, more cruel than she deserved. My grandmother and many other familial connections, exist for me only in faded black-and-white photographs.

Still, I've always loved an adventure in history! So, eager to see what awaited me, I set the teacup down, switched on the basement light and plunged down into the cool, vault-like darkness. There, as promised, I found two hoary cookbooks, one originally belonging to my Grandmother Edna, the other to her sister, my Great-Aunt Blanche.

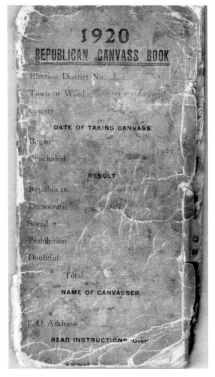

My grandmother's recipe book.

Turning the journals over in my hands, I got a scent of musty-smell, as they had spent years in obscurity, encased in plastic bags intended to ward off odors and the predations of bugs and dust and damp. Given their proximity to the Christmas decorations, I surmised that Mama must have stumbled across them recently while putting away the ornaments for another season, and just this moment remembered.

Like Indiana Jones, I handled these specimens carefully; not that I fancied some crazed elderly spirit might fly from them, but because they clearly meant a lot to my mother. These yellowed and crumbling but still legible notebooks were among the few relics she retains that bind her directly to the long-deceased mother she barely knew. My mother's mental images of Grandma Edna are those of a child: faint, almost dream-like. Still, the pervasive portrait, (buttressed by accounts from family and friends as my mother matured in Grandma's absence) painted a picture of my grandmother as a pretty blonde woman with a "pleasing countenance" as they say in the Bible. My mother has vague childhood memories of Grandma Edna giggling over a private joke with her friend Bertha, or chasing my mother her up the stairs in a moment of spontaneous play.

As my mother grew up, townspeople told her wistfully, "Your mother was just lovely. I can still see her, always laughing, always smiling." In fact, the local newspaper paid tribute to Grandma Edna, reporting: "She was a woman of the finest qualities and one who made friends with all with whom she came in contact." Grandma Edna appears to have been nothing less than a positive delight to nearly anyone who crossed paths with her, and a woman who, pre-marriage, was rarely photographed without a fuzzy cat or kitten in her arms, until such time as she acquired my mother and my two aunts to cuddle in snapshots.

Edna as a young woman

I knew that what I held in my hands was something special. Examining the worn brown cover of my grandmother's recipe collection, I saw that it read (curiously): "1920 Republican Canvass". Surely an odd choice for a receptacle of favorite recipes or "receipts" which was the parlance of bygone days? But my ancestors, springing from strong Dutch-German-American stock, were nothing if not frugal (farm families never knew whether this year's crop would be abundant or lean). The Canvass book was simply what came to hand in an opportune moment, an item that filled the bill when Grandma needed to put pen to paper.

I couldn't resist taking a quick peek inside, noticing the antique script and many misspellings ("rubarb" for rhubarb and "angles cake" for angel cake). Great-Aunt Blanche's collection was housed in a larger, black and white Composition notebook, of a style once used by every schoolchild in America. Blanche's book was stuffed like a Sunday chicken, with all manner of handwritten recipes and snippets of helpful household hints, such as remedies for "calf scours", what to do for a sick horse, and the best ways to keep white shoes clean. I realized my Mother wouldn't want me to unwrap this cache alone. These were truly gems—in every way, a "living" time capsule of early 20th century farm life.

When I got back upstairs to the kitchen, Mama took the books from me with care, the way you would handle a newborn baby. We gingerly opened the books, taking pains not to overly disturb the well-thumbed pages that clearly had been well-employed 90 years before, with great regularity, by my Grandmother and Great-Aunt. In that simple moment, I unlocked a treasure-trove of connections to my past—a past I had never fully grasped despite all the stories I'd heard about my mother's family. The names inscribed above each hand-written entry rolled off the tongue like something out of a Dickens novel: "(Pickle) Mrs. Barringer," "Jennie's Cream Cake, "and "Lottie's Hot Waffles Cake." The names atop the scribbles were old-fashioned, like Iola, Inez and Lila. And how generous that each cook was given her due, inscribed in the title, so one never forgot from whom this treat sprang! Clearly, my grandmother's contemporaries were on their honor to refrain from purloining a recipe that had been selflessly shared, then seizing upon it to claim it as their own. I could imagine that the full censure of the other ladies in their small town would come down on one's head, should she have the temerity to do so! And rightfully so, this was important business.

Reading through the recipes, you could almost feel the ancient, well-worn wooden spoons in your own hands, sense the way the women softened butter they had laboriously hand-churned themselves, creaming it with the sugar until all the elements mixed together harmoniously; the heady scent of vanilla and the earthy-smelling scoops of cocoa—resonating of a time when mastering the domestic arts was not just a necessity, but indeed, a creative outlet in a woman's life. These cakes and pies and casseroles were her "masterpieces"—celebrations of the small snatches of time a farm wife could spare from mundane chores for companionable get-togethers. That was an era where women worked equally hard in the field or orchards—and in the kitchen. Their domestic reputations were built on their abilities to whip up tasty cakes and pies, the most elaborate of which were reserved for the rare moments of leisure enjoyed at card parties, weddings, christenings and church suppers, tucked in amongst the hard reality of days of labor on the farm. For these women, whose lives were wrapped up in the day-to-day demands of keeping home and hearth humming, cooking was one way to express themselves and their personalities. Think of it: taking the raw materials of flour, eggs, sugar, butter, milk, salt, baking powder, baking soda and flavoring, and producing a foodstuff for all to admire—it's one of the most purely creative activities a human being can undertake. These cakes and pies, and "scalloped" casseroles, nourishing for both body and soul, were turned out in acts of generosity and love, and shared with those for whom they cared deeply.

The Coons family on a day out. Edna in back seat, middle

Missing from the receipts was any assignment of oven temperature, as the appliances of that time were cast iron woodstoves, the operation of which included all the attendant difficulties of lighting and maintaining a proper, steady temperature. Most of the recipes simply said, "in a slow oven," "in a hot oven," or "in a moderate oven". My mother remembers seeing the women of the family, in the morning, steadily feeding blocks of wood into the oven's gaping maw, consistently stoking and maintaining the temperature. Diverting your attention for even a few minutes, could result in a charred crusty mess when the batter got overheated, or a gloppy puddle if the temperature, like your cake, never rose to the occasion. My sense of wonder grew, with the discovery that some of the recipes in my grandmother's book, especially those cut out of magazines and journals, were quaintly affixed to the pages with straight-pins (Scotch tape not being invented until 1930). Again, the farm wife used what thrifty item came to hand to get the job done! So, with delight at the discoveries my fingers unlocked with each newly turned page, I embarked on a time-traveling journey through the past—a near-séance, if you will, with my female blood relatives. Was it foolishness to think that perhaps all of us, in some mystical sense, had joined hands at this moment around my own mother's 21st century kitchen?

Far from being outdated and unusable, many of these recipes can be altered for today's tastes for example, by substituting butter or margarine for lard or by ramping down the amount of sugar called for. The recipes are largely for sweets, which might explain why nearly every great-aunt and great-uncle on the maternal side of the family ended up with diabetes and/or heart disease. Still, some of the recipes are viable players in my mother's and my own repertoires. We turn to Gramma Coons' Sugar cookies, Aunt Jennie's Custard, or Salmon and Cracker Casserole when we crave a dose of old-style "comfort food". Some items speak to the economies of the times; crackers became a major "filler' item back in the pre-Depression and certainly, later, during the actual Great Depression era. On a cold winter night I have tucked into the sustaining strata of Salmon and Cracker Casserole, (freeform layers of saltines, onions, canned salmon, sprinkles of salt and pepper, doused with milk and baked until the top crisps up thanks to melty dollops of butter dropped on its crusty peaks) and in summer, Mama remembers her Aunt Jennie making Tomato-and -Cracker casserole (no better way to employ a bumper crop of tomatoes at the end of the season, than by—again!—layering crackers, tomatoes, onions, a pat of butter here, some salt and pepper there, and baking it the oven. I may as a rule, eschew these recipes in modern times as they are quite carbohydrate-heavy in this era of seemingly more enlightened eating. But when the occasion calls for a balm to soothe the ills and stresses of modern life, when you need to dip into the pool of family flavor-memories for nostalgia's sake, nothing will "cure what ails you", in the same satisfying way.

A hands-down family favorite is "Gramma Coons' Sugar Cookies," which my great-aunts and uncles called "cakes" or "drop cakes". In fact, historians will tell you that the original "cookies" came from cake recipes, tiny dollops of which were put in a hot oven to test that the conditions were right for inserting a big-version cake into the cooker. Still, the use of the specific word "cookie," a common, pres-ent-day usage in the United States, may derive from Dutch-speaking immigrants (many of which settled in Columbia County, New York) who used the word "koekje" to refer to these small treats. No matter what you want to call them, these sugar cookies, with a hint of lemon flavor, are like a beam of sunlight on a rainy day.

Like the British custom of traditional teatime—a stalwart still observed in this hurly-burly modern world—stopping for a "cuppa" with a sweet cake on the side simply elevates that discrete five min-ute "time-out" in our frazzled, harried existences. It's a short break—as we halt the madness of our whirligig lives—carved out like a slice of custard pie, where we can stop, savor, enjoy, and be truly "in the moment". These cookies are just that transporting—they are com-fort and joy wrapped up in a tiny parcel of crumbs. Many years after Grandma Edna baked them (following a recipe her own mother and grandmother—the original Gramma Coons—used), this recipe pro-duces stellar results you will want to share with family and friends.

Gramma Coons' Sugar Cookies (For modern cooks)

(Modern Version with time and temperature for cooking)

¼ cup shortening (Crisco, for example) mixed with ¼ cup butter or margarine

1 cup sugar

2 eggs

2 cups flour

1 and ½ teaspoon baking powder

½ cup milk

¼ teaspoon salt

1 teaspoon vanilla

½ teaspoon lemon extract

1 cup raisins

Mix shortening, sugar, eggs, vanilla and lemon extract until well combined. In a separate bowl, mix flour, baking powder, salt. Mix the dry ingredients into the wet ingredients in measures, alternating with the ½ cup of milk. Add raisins. Drop in teaspoonfuls on a lightly greased cookie sheet. Bake 10 minutes at 375 degrees until golden brown on the edges.

Gramma Coons at her home.

It occurs to me that it is no small gift to be handed a well-worn book, especially something that was routinely turned over in the hands of my antecedent nearly a century ago. It's as if, by touching this inanimate object, I can almost reach out and touch *her*...to uncover in some small way the mysteries of a woman I never met but to whom I owe my very existence. Recipe books have lives of their own, giving off a whiff of the former chef's essence, with every page stained by bubbled-over pie filling, every bit of cocoa powder still couched in the cracks of the binding. Cooking, in so many ways, is the "connective tissue" that bonds me with the grandmother I never knew, and employing her tried-and-true recipes honors her, and all the other women on the family tree who came before me.

But these are so much more than just recipes. I wonder what triumphs and joys, what failures and losses got stirred up with the batter while Grandma Edna stood at the kitchen counter? What internal monologue accompanied the swoosh, swoosh, swoosh of wooden spoon against ceramic bowl? In concert with the spoon traversing the bowl's circumference, the world was spinning around outside: children playing and growing up, family businesses failing or prospering, marriage bonds waxing or waning, age creeping up on them whether they were ready for it or not.

Gramma Coons,
Edna's grandmother

At a minimum, cooking and baking provides sustenance to keep the family going forward, every day; for some of us it is a mundane chore, but without it, how could generations have survived down the centuries?

What is the first thing that happens once we've been yanked into the world at birth? After drawing our initial breath, and uttering that clarion infant cry, the answer is: we are fed. So why wouldn't we be obsessed with this life-affirming action that comes to us as naturally as breathing?

So, I ask myself, who was Edna Catherine Coons Yager? Without her, I surely would not exist. How do I, 90 years later, reach out to someone so crucial to my very being?

October, 1920

Edna bent over a small notebook at her bedroom desk and glanced out the window overlooking the orchard. She marveled at the golden-russet color, like in those old-fashioned sepia-toned photographs. It spread across the farm in its autumnal state, leaves cast down by the trees in preparation for the winter ahead. It was October, and there was still plenty to do on the family fruit farm. In the packing house, the gathering up of the bumper apple crop for final sale was in full swing. A series of warm days followed by cool, crisp nights, had culti-vated the rich, red beauties dangling off the tree branches, whose sale would fill the coffers of the Coons family. They had tended to them so diligently all season, surely Pa would declare this a good year! She could hear the shouts of the men as they began putting away their tools and wrapping up their day's work. A frisson of anticipation ran through her and she suppressed a tiny giggle; she smoothed down the page and wrote her first entry on the unblemished lined paper in the notebook. She had been in a hurry, and casting about for something on which to write, and had seized upon, of all things, a "1920 Republi-can Canvass Book" sent to the Coons family from New York City GOP Headquarters. On the overleaf inside, it gave names of party officials with strict instructions that the canvass would be used simultane-ously as a mailing list and registration of voters. It emphasized the importance of strict adherence to party rules, exhorting that all names be written down "plainly and correctly" while the Canvasser endeav-ored to, "If possible, ascertain from each voter personally for whom he or she intends to vote. If the voter is undecided, put such voter down as 'Doubtful'." New York State had been the first Eastern State to fully enfranchise women; but just two months ago it was made the law of the land across the United States, by the 19th Constitutional amendment. Edna remembered the furor and letters to the editor of *"The Rural New Yorker,"* a farm-news-cum-household-tips publication that Ma and Pa read faithfully each week, from cover to cover. On the back of a recipe entitled "Mother's Gingerbread," (Preceded by the information that:" Yes, boys do cook, for here is a gingerbread recipe from one of our New Hampshire boys") that Edna had snipped out of the magazine for safekeeping, a lady named Olive Schreiner had written *"We women demand the franchise and this and that from man—it is not the man who can enfranchise us, but we who must enfranchise ourselves, we who must free ourselves from the bondage of the mean and trivial which eats out our women's souls..."**

Edna looked out the window to see the sun sinking down low on the horizon. She was all for a woman having rights, but it just wasn't in her makeup to go out and march and protest and carry signs like the suffragettes she had seen in the newspaper photographs. Truth be told, all she'd ever really desired was to be a wife and mother and preside over her very own home and family. And now, that dream was going to come true!

Edna had stolen these few moments of time alone, knowing that the men would be coming in to dinner in a few minutes; in the heart of harvest time they would be truly famished after a hard day's work. She heard Ma clanging pots and pans downstairs and heard the clink of dishes being set out and forks, spoons and knives arranged like soldiers at attention in their places on the table. Truly, she reveled in this private moment. Having eight brothers and sisters under one roof meant that being able to steal away to enjoy a simple minute—just to yourself—was a supreme and utter luxury! And how delicious to have a book of pristine pages in front of you—a ready vessel to be filled with whatever words came to mind, pregnant with possibilities like, well, like Life itself.

*Believed to be from "The Rural New Yorker"- date unknown. Original quote: Copyright Olive Schreiner Letters Project. Olive Schreiner to Sarah Ann Tooley, 1897.NLSA Cape Town Special Collections, Olive Schreiner Letters Project (transcription, lines 103-107)

Clarence Yager

What she entered on the page now, what she was fixing to transcribe with her pen, would be for posterity, a cornerstone to her very future, a gateway to the destiny she'd always dreamed of. Wonder of wonders, Clarence Yager had proposed!

Of course Edna had known Clarence all of his life. She was literally the "girl next door," as the Coons family farm and the Yager family farm sat adjacent to each other and could be accessed by walking "cross-lots". But Clarence had always hung around the older boys and had no time for younger girls like her. Until about a year ago, when she caught him staring at her in church; both of them quickly turned their heads back to their hymnals when their eyes locked, but something—something—was different after that.

While she wouldn't hear of such talk in her presence (and gently upbraided others who mentioned it—except for dear Clarence of course, she *would* allow him, as her betrothed, that liberty), Edna was generally spoken of by others to be the prettiest girl in the Coons family: sweet of disposition, always seen laughing with friends. Her sisters (Jennie, Jessie, Blanche) were either plump and jowly, or sharp-featured, less- than-beauties; they had also inherited the Coons family's negative tendency to quickly tamp down high spirits or prideful talk (especially in younger members of the family) by loudly pronouncing: "You're not gonna amount to nawthin' more than you are right now."

Edna, by contrast, had a positive outlook, and was generally welcomed as a "breath of fresh air" in most company. Her blonde hair was swept up into a somewhat loose, Gibson-girl style bun. She had ice-blue eyes, offset by her warm smile and warm heart. That compassion extended not only to her fellow humans but to four-legged creatures as well; cats and kitties were her very favorite farm animal, by far. In the company of others, Edna was quick to smile and to make the other person feel at ease—so was it any wonder that Clarence Yager fell hard for her charms?

Edna turned back to her notebook. Instead of ticking off the boxes "Republican, Democrat, Socialist, Prohibition, Doubtful, First Voter, Enrolled Republican, Enrolled Democrat, Voted Last Election," she carefully inscribed "Caroline's Spice Cake" on the first page.

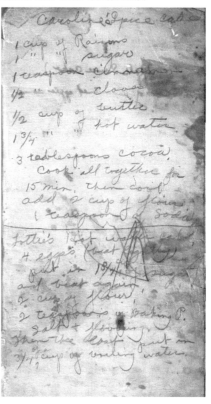

Caroline's Spice Cake

Caroline's Spice Cake

 1 cup of raisins
 1 cup of sugar
 1 teaspoonful cinnamon
 ½ teaspoonful cloves
 ½ cup butter
 1 ¾ cup of hot water
 3 Tablespoons cocoa

Cook it all together for 15 minutes, then cool. Add 2 cups of flour, 1 teaspoon of soda

Bake in a moderate oven. (Note: A moderate oven is set at about 350 degrees)

They had set the date for their wedding: April 21st, 1921. Like other young wives-to-be, Edna wanted to put down a good collection of recipes so she could refer to them when she began running her very own home. How different her life would be! Clarence was dark-haired and handsome, with a noble brow; people called him an "up-and-coming" young man, who had a vast fruit farm of nearly 100 acres, which he ran for his parents, who still lived with him in the farmhouse. People in town still talked about the time headstrong Clarence wanted a brand-new autocar so desperately, that he sat under a tree and refused to work the farm until his father granted him one. Once Clarence was determined about something, he usually won. Of course Clarence felt he deserved the car as he was the diligent, hard-working child in the Yager family, unlike his brother Byron. Byron was, it had to be admitted, something of a wastrel. As was Byron's wife Fanny. Byron and Fanny were fond of the drink, which was a source of quiet shame but never spoken of in the Yager family. Amazingly, Clarence's father Abram turned a blind eye to Byron's profligacy, even though years before, Abram had caused town gossips to titter behind his back, when he and the Reformed Church *domine** launched a homegrown temperance movement, taking planks of wood and nailing the town saloon doors shut! Such was their revulsion for alcohol and its slavish devotees. Yet, outwardly, Abram acted as if Byron was the soul of sobriety, bestowing upon Byron and Fanny their own piece of

Byron Yager, Clarence's brother

farmland in Stottville. Of course, to Clarence's consternation, Clarence was the one expected to travel ten miles to the north, and help Abram work Byron's farm, in addition to his own large spread, when Byron and Fanny were "in their cups". It was so unjust, Edna thought, in defense of poor Clarence. Byron was loved like a modern version of the Prodigal Son, while Clarence was the responsible, but unfavored child. Ah, are parents ever equitable to their offspring? Edna pledged to herself never to play favorites with her own young ones, which she dearly hoped God would be good enough to bestow on the young couple, once-married.

---

*Domine- *from the Dutch, meaning Protestant minister (pronounced doh'-min-ee)*

Like many in their small town, Edna had left school after the 8th grade, and that was enough for her. Contrary to her experience, Clarence had a true zeal for learning and knowledge. He distinguished himself as a "cut above" the rest, by attending Albany Business College, about 40 miles north of their town, in the state Capital, for a year. He wore the mantle of a man who had attained higher education. After he delivered truckloads of fruit down to New York City at the massive produce market there, he would travel north through the city on the way home and stop off to hear portions of what were called "open air" lectures at various public squares. That's where he got his ideas about the salubrious effects of fresh air, after listening to one of the professors pontificate about its healthful qualities. Consequently, he threw open the house windows even in the harsh dead of winter. Ma and Pa and everyone Edna had grown up with always proclaimed that "night air is harmful". But Clarence had more sophisticated ideas. (She would have to make certain her trousseau included a warm woolly blanket!). His forward-thinking even extended to modern sanitation. After soaking up what the New York City pundits were offering one week, Clarence boasted, "No wife of mine will go without indoor plumbing!" As good as his word, he had already set things into motion at his farmhouse, so she would have a working indoor bathroom (such a luxury!) when they crossed the threshold as Man and Wife.

Yes, sometimes people said Clarence was a little loud when proclaiming his thoughts and opinions but wasn't that because he was a man of conviction? She heard the old clock in the hall chime "one-two-three-four-five". 5 pm on the dot. At this moment, Clarence would be strapping down the contents of the truck bed, preparing in just a few hours' time, to make that weekly night-pilgrimage to New York. He would arrive in the city around midnight, bearing crates and bushels of fruits for the teeming Washington Market that flourished in the city's late night, while farmers upstate snored in their beds. Clarence had described the colorful scene so many times, she could picture it in her mind. Oh, how she wished that one day she might see it for herself!

The wee-hours activity there was as vibrant as if it were the middle of the day in other people's worlds; the market bristled and bustled with commerce in the dark. Harsh overhead lights sent illuminating shafts to the stalls below, as a cacophony of shouts rose and the fumes of fuel from idling trucks wound themselves around the proceedings. Merchants purveying fruits and produce—and in other nearby markets, meats and eggs and all manner of unusual delicacies—got down to business so all would be set for their urban customers who appeared, sometimes at the crack of dawn. The produce was set out in neat rows, glistening wet from a hose-down, intended to give the appearance that they had just been plucked from the tree in the morning dew. Beyond the covered fruit and produce area, farmers jockeyed their trucks for a good parking space where they could unload their wares. Truck springs creaking with the weight of hauled fruit, Clarence would pull into a likely spot and start lifting down this week's offering, which he hoped to sell for a decent price to his friend, the commission merchant, Max Mandel. Spying Clarence, Mandel hastily wiped his hands on his handkerchief, offered a firm shake and asked, "Well, my friend, what do you have for me this week?" He seized one or two of the apples for appraisal, trusting that the entire bushel was quality product right to the bottom of the basket. Street urchins with grimy faces, scraps of clothing and mere straps of leather holding their shoes together, would sneak near the trucks to see if they could snatch fruit that had fallen off as the farmer unloaded.

Clarence explained to Edna that while most people used the general term "Washington Market," late in the last century, it had started with two distinct markets: the Farmer's or Gansevoort Market for produce and the West Washington Market for poultry, meat and dairy products. It was a joy for Clarence to rub elbows with his fellow farmers from all around the region there, and he felt every bit the prosperous agrarian among them. After all, this was the epitome of city markets, a spot that boasted all manner of fruits, vegetables, meats and delicacies traded there. Many felt the Washington Market rivaled the great food halls of London and Paris. Clarence said that in the early 1900s, up-to-date refrigeration lines had been laid down underground, making it tremendously easy to keep foods fresh for longer intervals of time. Increasingly, the wares exchanged at the market were feeding the bustling steamship and hotel industry now operating out of New York City. It made a man proud to be a farmer, Clarence declared to Edna, knowing that what he had tended and harvested from mere seeds in the soil in a small town in upstate New York, was going to feed thousands, from working class folks of Manhattan, to the well-heeled travelers on luxury steamship liners, headed to Europe.

The upper Hudson Valley where they lived was certainly the "fruit-bowl" to vast swaths of the Northeast. Edna's Pa had a thriving farm, but Clarence's father, Abram Yager, was rumored to have $100,000 in the bank (Clarence's Aunt Lilly being a bit free with information she probably shouldn't have shared with just anyone in town). Clarence stood to inherit a good portion of that. Of course, Clarence's father Abram and his mother Carrie, still lived with him on the farm, but Clarence, once he had proposed, promised Edna that she would not have to share a house with his difficult mother Carrie.

Carrie Yager, Edna's mother-in-law

"We'll split the house in two," Clarence said heartily, practically willing Edna to go along with the idea. "We'll take the six rooms on the West side of the house and Father and Mother will take the six rooms on the East side of the house." Realizing that the prospect of sharing a home with an older female—especially a difficult, opinionated mother-in-law—might cause Edna some consternation, Clarence hastily added: "You and my Mother will have separate kitchens, so she won't interfere with you and your domestic chores." Edna knew how hard it was for two adult women to share the same kitchen; her sister Blanche shared a kitchen with a sister-in-law, as both couples resided in the same house. Even though she was her sister, Edna had to admit that stout Blanche was something of a battleaxe who tried to boss around sweet-tempered sister-in-law Caroline something fierce. It was a tough row to hoe, but Caroline managed to do it with grace and dignity, generally acquiescing to whatever Blanche felt was best for the sake of peace under their roof. Thankfully, Edna wouldn't have to submit to Carrie Yager's interference in the kitchen and interfere she surely would try to do.

Edna sighed. She didn't want to let her joy at being proposed to, at anticipating a new status in life as a married woman, be dampened by the thought of forced proximity to Clarence's mother. Carrie Yager. Ma had always said (not unkindly), "That Carrie Yager is—a little—touched in the head." Without question, thought Edna, Carrie would make a formidable mother-in-law. When she and Clarence had broken the news of their engagement to Edna's family, there had been laughter and rejoicing and much joking and elbows-in-the-sides between her brothers and sisters. Not so when they were ushered into the cold dark sanctuary that was the parlor of Abram and Carrie Yager, for what proved to be a tepid reception. "We're getting married!" announced Clarence in that hearty way he had; usually his enthusiasm and brio carried the day and the spirits of the others assembled. But not Carrie. While Abram rushed to give Edna a chaste peck on the cheek and to pump Clarence's hand up and down in congratulations, Edna couldn't fail to see Carrie turn away with that same sour expression on her face she'd seen dozens of times at church services. Carrie was furious. Abram, sensing a gap where there should have been cries of joy, tried to make up for his wife's lack of enthusiasm for the planned union by clapping his son on the back and saying "Wonderful, my boy! Great news!" Carrie, with her hair pulled back severely, had a manner even more austere. She remained silent and shortly after they had announced their betrothal, said she was going upstairs to bed. No congratulations, no felicitations. In fact, she appeared to be inwardly seething. Not that Edna was really surprised. She was aware from talk in the town that Carrie considered the Coons family inferior. Oh certainly, Pa was a well-to-do farmer who even owned stocks and visited the New York Stock Exchange from time to time to check on his investments. But Carrie referred to the Coonses as "common," because Ma had borne 14 children in all, five of which had not survived to adulthood. Carrie felt that being so prolific with offspring was rather less than genteel. But perhaps it stemmed from jealousy on Carrie's part, because of the great loss she had suffered years ago.

When Ma referred to Carrie as being "a little off", she always cushioned what might have seemed unduly harsh by saying, "Of course, that's since she lost Edith". Everyone said Carrie had not been the same since her last-born child and only daughter Edith had died of diphtheria at age eight. Everyone said how beautiful Edith was, clear-eyed and sweet-dispositioned. Carrie was inconsolable when they lost Edith, and over the years her grief had taken a bitter, inward turn. Clarence confided that after Edith's death, nothing about his mother had ever seemed right again. Yet, thought Edna, even though Ma had given birth to 14 children, she had suffered the same kind of grief five times over. When they vis-

Edith Yager, Clarence's sister.

ited the Dutch Reformed Church Cemetery, she sometimes spied Ma wistfully rubbing her finger across the names on the headstones of Edna's prematurely deceased siblings: Melvin, Kitty, Harry, Maggie and Everitt. Except for Melvin, who died at 17, the others had succumbed to one disease or another in early childhood. Yes, Ma had also endured the worst loss a mother could bear: having to bury your own child. Yet while Ma still mourned over her lost babies in private moments, she didn't take her grief out on the rest of the world. Ma realized that the surviving children and the rest of the family also needed her.

Later that night, when Edna had returned home, and Carrie was alone with Abram, Carrie angrily spat out a day's worth of venom that had been simmering since Clarence announced his betrothal.

"Low-class, those Coonses! "she said, eyes flashing, defying her husband to object.

Again, Abram rose to their soon-to-be-daughter-in-law's defense.

"Now Carrie, you just stop. She's a lovely girl, who will make a splendid wife for our Clarence. You'll see..."

"Edna!" bellowed a voice from downstairs, jolting her back to the present. It was her brother Chauncey. "Ma needs you to help with the potatoes!!" Edna permitted herself a moment to think about Clarence...a good-looking man, with dark wavy hair, and full lips. She knew some of

Coons Family dog, Webster (father), Esther (Edna's mother), Foster (brother), Jessie, Blanche, Jennie (sisters), Edna

the other girls thought him handsome. Her mind cast back to last Sunday, after church, when she spotted that Claudette Hoak sidling up to Clarence, chatting with him in her ingratiating way. Claudette had always seemed sweet on him, and was forever manufacturing a way to snatch his attention, putting her hand on his arm, always shortening the space between them at any gathering. But, at that very moment, Clarence had happened to look up, caught Edna's eye across the church yard and winked at her. Claudette had followed his gaze, and put on a sour pout when she realized he only had eyes for Edna. She murmured excuses unheard by anyone and abruptly turned on her heel to leave. Yes, Edna's heart was full. She knew Clarence was considered a good prospect for a husband. She was satisfied that at long last, she had made what the neighborhood ladies called, "a catch"!

Tucking away that thought in a secret mental compartment, she reluctantly yanked herself out of her reverie and dashed down the stairs to help with the supper.

April, 1921

Edna took a last look at the dining room table and did a quick inventory: Cream cake, pound cake, rhubarb conserves, lemon meringue pie, nut-meats, lemonade, coffee, tea, cream and sugar. Jennie had transformed the austere dining room into a bower of beauty; daffodils draped themselves languidly over the rims of the family's best cut glass vases, tulips stood at attention, and tucked in amongst the larger blooms were a few violets, whose tiny faces spread out in what seemed to be smiles on this auspicious day. She looked up at her reflection in the dining room mirror—the glass festooned with crepe paper—and smiled at what she saw. Married! She was getting married! In just a few hours, she would look in the mirror and then, she would be Mrs. Clarence Yager, good and proper.

Edna ran her hands down the heavy damask tablecloth that Ma had spent all last night pressing, putting the heavy iron on the hot, hot stove, then pulling it out at just the right moment, taking care not to singe the white table covering with a triangular black scorch mark. Everything had been laid out in readiness for the Big Day. Edna realized that she was feeling quite sentimental today, on this grand and auspicious occasion on which she would "enter into holy wedlock," as she had heard the minister say at perhaps a dozen other weddings in her lifetime. This day, which would change the course of her life. Up until now, she thought, her life had been uneventful, circumscribed by existence on this farm. She looked out the window at the neatly spaced rows and rows and rows of trees that went on as far as the eye could see. Trees that had sustained her family for—what was it—centuries now? Her ancestors came from Germany's Southwestern region. The Palatinate of their homeland had also been situated near a river—two of them, to be precise, the Rhine and the Moselle. Her people had joined the Great Migration of 1709, leaving their native Germany like thousands of others, some of whom stopped briefly in Holland and in England where they made passage to the New World. Those early forebears had sailed up the Hudson River (much like Henry Hudson for whom it is named) and settled in these verdant, rolling hills of Columbia County. They left harsh conditions in Europe and set to work in the New World, tending the land of the Patroon,* or the first Lord of the Manor, Robert Livingston. Among the many towns that sprang up along the East banks of the Hudson River, was this settlement originally called "East Camp," but now called Germantown, in a nod to the ancestry of many who lived there. Still, the influence of Dutch settlers was undeniable in the development of the tiny town and this whole region, 100 miles north of New York City. Didn't she and her family all attend the *Dutch* Reformed Church, after all? In fact, while they surely had German blood in their genes (Coons was probably originally "Kuhn" in the old country), at the advent and even after the recent conclusion of the Great War, Edna's family had become accustomed to saying "We're Holland Dutch," so there would be no suspicion that their family might be sympathizers with the Kaiser. Outside, the cherry trees had taken on a distinctly pink aura, as their blossoms prepared to burst forth from the branches. Momma barn cat, swollen pregnant belly nearly brushing the ground, slunk under a tree to groom herself as she awaited the arrival of a litter of kittens. The very soil underfoot felt fertile. Apples, berries, cherries, plums, peaches, pears—they were the bread and butter of the Coons' family existence, and of the Yager family, which she would be formally and irrevocably joining in mere hours. Did her forebears have the same love for the rich soil, which, with diligence, favorable weather and tender loving care, brought forth bushels and bushels of sustaining fruit? Did they stop in the summer's heat to wipe their brows, survey their little plot and acknowledge that their labors were not simply a vocation, but a calling?

---

* *patroons – Patrons, masters (Dutch)*

Edna let the curtain fall back, as she turned to the table to resume her inspection. Upon spying the rhubarb conserves, she had to suppress a chuckle, as they had become something of a family joke now. Her brother Stanley never missed an opportunity to tell the story when rhubarb season was upon them.

Rubarb (sic) conserves 3 lbs of Rubarb
> 3 lbs of sugar
> 1 lb raisins
> 1 orange
> nuts
>
> 20 minutes (boil until thickened)

Recipe for "Rubarb Conserves"

According to family lore, one particular stab at hospitality involving "the help" ended in a clear culinary—if not personal health-and-hygiene—disaster.

The story went that Jim, the hired hand, was for some now-forgotten reason, invited up to the "big house" one evening to take dinner with the Coons family.

What Jim could not have known (and had he, he might have run for the hills) was that Edna and her sisters, in an effort to be fashionable, routinely saved the hair harvested from their hand brushes to fashion small, oval coiffure aids they called "rats". It was not a family trait amongst the females in the Coons clan to be celebrated for having a "crowning glory" of lustrous hair. Through the generations their struggles with coiffure were a constant exasperation, as they tried to wrangle recalcitrant tresses into shape each and every morning. So, these "rats" as they were called, were composed of tangled strands of hair that were shaped into small nests that one could pin close to one's scalp, disguising their presence by deftly combing the existing strands of hair over the top, giving the illusion of height and volume. In what turned out to be a case of extremely poor judgment, the girls had opted to keep their "rats" in the pantry—as it happened, on the shelf just above the put-up jam jars and conserves.

Come supper time, the spread was laid out and Jim arrived, freshened up from fruit farm labors, clean-shaven, dark hair slicked back flat on his head. Unfortunately, he chose to partake of some biscuits that had been laid out and quite liberally spread his portion with homemade conserves. Unbeknownst to his hosts, the girls' "rats" had fallen into the conserves and at some point had become entangled with the jam, indiscernible to the naked eye. Imagine the horror of those assembled, as they silently watched a stupefied Jim tentatively pull strand after strand of cast-off hair from his mouth! Once they'd realized what happened, they all had a good laugh, and Ma ran to get another uncontaminated jam from the pantry, thankfully checking it for hair strands before setting it out on the table!

"Edna dear, it's time to go," said Pa who broke her reverie, as he stood framed by the doorway, looking rather sad, yet proud. How long had he been standing there? Edna got the feeling he'd been watching her, his youngest girl, and feeling sentimental today for his very own reasons.

"I'm ready, Pa," she said smiling shyly. She fitted her arm through the crook of his elbow, and they walked through the door and into her New Life.

Berries, June 2007

"Sophie, what do you *have*???" I asked, slightly exasperated, as I walked my ten-month-old Siberian Husky puppy in the back yard. Sophie is a law unto herself: clever, high-spirited, and despite my occasional impatience, a general joy to be around. "Pup-zuberance!!" is how my husband Denis describes her bonhomie, requiring that she be under constant surveillance, as curiosity is her "default" setting.

Consequently, she is always getting into one thing or another that you probably would prefer she steered well clear of. As I brought up the leash to corral her, I could see that she was nibbling at something in a clutch of thorny bushes. She daintily tried to navigate her tongue around a profusion of branches, delicately biting at one of the protrusions. "Whoa! Did you just find our berry bushes?" I asked her, as she plucked one and gobbled her prize quickly, lest I attempt to intervene. The first summer we lived here, we never did find the "raspberries" the former owner alluded to, when laying out the many qualities of the 6.1 acres of which we were about to take possession. There were so many questions to ask about other things—the septic system, the well, the pony barn—we just figured raspberries would be self-evident, like the truths we hold in the Declaration of Independence. After that first summer in the country came and went, I figured I must have dreamed the whole thing up. But here they were, like little jewels, sparkling in the post-dawn dew and gathering sun of a summer morning.

What joy to find them right here on the property, in an era where, when the faintest "food mood" strikes us, it must be satisfied in seconds! We grab the keys, fire up the car's engine and race off to the closest emporium that offers the comestibles of which we cannot rid our senses. Inevitably, the acquisition of what we seek is something of a disappointment; what you buy is barely ripe or overripe or requires the negotiation of a small bank loan to procure even a tiny quantity, insufficient for making a sturdy, bursting-with-juices pie or crock of toast-slathering homemade jam—that you throw up your hands in disgust hours later, wondering what, in fact, was the point of all that effort?

So, what an unparalleled delight to be able to simply go outdoors in your sandals and pluck from the abundance just waiting there for your delectation! The earth offers it up; it's your due, you are the landlord. The parallels to the Garden of Eden are not lost on me, I assure you. And I wonder whether my ancestors, despite fruit farming being their family business, had that same thrill every year? The abundance of the land is extended with complete largesse, no *quid pro quo*, no expectations of recompense other than that you do your level best to keep on tending and harvesting what springs from the soil? Did my forebears get a similar charge from gathering the raw materials for foodstuff from their own property—that deep-down sense of reward I get from overseeing the process of creating a pie from berry bush to plate? We foolishly put this down to "modern" thinking, but could my Grandmother have had this same sense of wonder, of stewardship of the land?

To my surprise, one of the unbridled joys of living out in the country is having the space and amenities available to grow your own food. After the initial berry discovery, we learned that every June and July the land churned forth bumper crops of the sweet, tart, darkly delicious fruit. Our weather conditions are usually exactly right for berry production, with reliable tiny jewels bursting forth each season, purple, plump and juicy.

Still, harvesting them is not for the faint of heart. To achieve success, you must have the soul, the perseverance, the intestinal fortitude of a Medieval Knight seeking the hand of the Princess Fair. The thorny branches do not give up their progeny easily, believe me. I endure multiple scratches as I plunge in, wondering what ill-tempered fauna I might unintentionally tread upon, as I step down into the tangle of weeds and bushes. Once it's begun, I grab the berries off the branches greedily, even as I look for more that have ripened to maturity, knowing that their season is short and they must be used to the utmost. I have now perfected a technique where I grasp the branch and gently roll the little buttons off their clusters, avoiding the anemic not-ripened, the near-ripened, and the day-away-from-truly-ripened. It takes patience and forbearance; you must not snatch them when they're not fully incubated. Any shade of red is best left to a day or more under the warming ministrations of Old Sol. The ideal berries are near-black in color, and feel as if they are just barely containing the ripples of nectar that would be unleashed once tooth bit fruit. The early morning Sun dapples through the branches, and as I bend down to pick the low-hanging fruit, I realize that the juiciest specimens don't live at the highest altitudes where they are exposed to the elements, but rather in the shade, under the protective cover of the green leaves. A corona of insects swarms about my head, intent on taking up residence in my eyes, further complicating what should be a simple task.

I've learned that once you pluck your prize, the thorny stems don't give it up without a fight. Many is the time I have seized a berry, only to have the nearby stems rip across the flesh of my legs and arms with the ferocity of a Momma bear defending her precious cub. Half the time, once I've nearly extricated myself from the battlefield, the thorns give me a parting blow for good measure, as I exit the patch. But the sacrifice is well worth the effort, as you sink your teeth into the succulent gems, rewarded by a spurt of sweet-tart juice, tasting of the promise of endless summer.

Last night I cooked up the berries in a saucepan with some sugar, lemon juice, cornstarch to thicken, and added water, then chucked the thick warm mélange into a homemade piecrust "cozy," and put it in the oven at 425 degrees for about 30 minutes. A bouncy, bubbling, delectable pie came out, which we enjoyed immensely.

December, 1921

Edna padded across the freezing kitchen floor in her stocking feet and pulled her too-thin wrapper tightly around her. Her robe was increasingly unable to contain her ever-swelling midsection, since she was, as they say in the Bible, "great with child". Happily, she didn't have to trek to the outhouse in the freezing cold, thanks to Clarence, who, good as his word, had proudly installed that new indoor bathroom on their side of the house to impress his bride.

The winter morning's chill, before the house got warmed up, was particularly sharp over the past few days. The minute you opened the door in the morning, cold blasts of frigid air crashed their way into the house, like unwanted guests. Edna stepped quickly outside most mornings to give a small warmed saucer of milk to the Momma kitty, who ingratiatingly wound her lithe body around Edna's ankles. Perhaps she wanted to be invited in, to luxuriate in the warmth generated by the woodstove once it was going good and hot. Foolish to treat a cat like a queen, but it made Edna happy to know she had helped sustain a small creature, not to mention her kittens, who were facing the elements just as humans must.

Germantown was experiencing a particularly cold snap this early in the winter. Outside it was nearly too cold for the men to go out and inspect the trees for trimming, which was one of their main jobs this time of year. You had to wait until the trees were dormant, and be vigilant for dead or diseased limbs, snipping back suckers in the mid-to-late-winter so there would be full, glorious blooms in the springtime. Springtime seemed eons away this bitter-cold morning. Edna cast an eye toward the water steaming in the reservoir on the side of the cast iron stove. It had to be heated up to a temperature suitable for Clarence to do his shaving once he came inside after tackling the initial chores around the farm.

She sorted through the box of kindling next to the cast iron wood stove. The stove was slightly different from the one she was used to in Ma's kitchen, so it had taken her a while to get the knack of stoking the fire to get it appropriately hot. First, you had to feed in the kindling and light a match to paper to make the fire catch. Then shove the poker into the embers, to make steady flames arise. Edna mused that this was a good day to take the chill off with crullers and nice hot waffles. She'd have to remember to set aside a dozen crullers for Dossie's wife, who was also pregnant and much closer to delivery of her child than Edna. Dossie was their hired hand, who came up from the South where a man of his color had very little chance to get ahead in life. They worked the orchards alongside Clarence and the rest of the family, and Edna hoped that even though they lived in a small shack on the property, their lot was better here in the North than it would have been back in the South. Edna remembered practicing her penmanship with a flourish, writing the name "Henry Ward Beecher"—or was it "Henry Ward Beacher"? Spelling was never her strong suit! All Edna remembered from her education before leaving upon completion of the 8th grade was that Beecher had been a noted abolitionist of his day. Pity, that business about whispers and rumors involving Beecher and a married lady. They didn't teach about all *that* in school.

Back in the day, abolition of slavery was welcomed and supported in Clarence's family. Clarence's grandfather Jacob had been an engineer on a Hudson River tugboat, which regularly made trips from Hudson down to New York City and back north. What hadn't been freely talked about at the time was that those tugs often smuggled up escaped slaves from the South. Clarence's father told of how, in the 1850s and 1860s, the family hid slaves in the cellar overnight in this very house, when the tug stopped in Hudson. The Yagers were among those local folks helping them to make their way to safety, either elsewhere in the north or most likely in Canada. Could she have borne such circumstances, fleeing for her life, perhaps with little children in tow? How terrified those poor souls must have been, Edna thought, stuck in a cold damp basement, waiting for passage, utterly dependent on the kindness and good graces of these northern white folks who aimed to help them to a better life. The fugitives were shepherded out of their hiding places, under the cover of darkness at two or three in the morning and—it was hoped, as you never heard what happened to them—spirited to freedom.

Jacob Yager, tug boat engineer and Clarence's grandfather

It was a dangerous business back then. A man like Jacob Yager could have gotten into trouble for aiding and abetting. In the mid-1800s, these people were considered "property" down South. Edna shook her head, as if to get the distasteful idea of "owning" a human being out of her mind. Even though he was a child at the time, her father-in-law vividly remembered emotions running high just after President Lincoln had been assassinated. Abram said he would never forget the scene he witnessed when he accompanied his father to the local General Store just after hearing the news that Lincoln had been shot. People stood in disbelief and shock, murmuring their despair over the President's death. But one man from town—never a Lincoln supporter—had the nerve at that moment to grumble, "Good!" In an instant, Abram said, the red-faced storekeeper had leapt over the counter in a rage, thrashing the man for his disrespect to their departed leader.

Edna leafed through her recipes, planning her day ahead. In addition to Dossie and his family, there was another among their farm workers, an older man, who should also be the recipient of her baking today: "Old Pete", the Polish émigré, who lived in a ramshackle structure on the property and was a particular friend of her father-in-law, Abram. They were from completely different backgrounds; her father-in-law had some education, and was a businessman and landowner. Pete, by contrast, had very little schooling, and even as a man in his sixties, still had to work for another man to make his living. Yet, somehow, they seemed to strike up a friendship, these two old men—perhaps advanced age being their common denominator? Dozens of times Edna had watched Old Pete's fingers, gnarled with arthritis but still fairly nimble, as they sorted apples in the packing house, years of experience allowing them to deftly separate the good fruit from the wormy and the bruised. She knew that given his "druthers", the elderly man would have been happy to sit at home by the warming fire. Still, he had to do something to earn money to live. Yes, Life could be brutal to the aged, so if there was some small treat she might bake for him to brighten his day, was that too much to ask? Certainly not!

No more lollygagging now, thought Edna, time for breakfast. The kettle had finally started to boil for coffee. At the very least, Clarence would want a steaming cup of coffee after feeding the animals, yet he wasn't much on eating a huge morning meal. Good, she noted, the water in the reservoir on the side of the stove had warmed up sufficiently so Clarence could have a proper wash-up.

Edna pulled out the spider* and allowed herself a minute to sit down in the heavy oak rocking chair. She drew a shawl over herself as the fire began to roar, and got back to her recipe book. It had been a long time since she'd made "Lottie's Hot Waffles." Clarence deserved a "stick-to-your-ribs" breakfast on a chilly morning like this one. Edna liked having the house all to herself, in the stillness of the morning, before Clarence came back in from the morning chores. There were always cows to milk, pigs and chickens to feed, broken fences to mend. Yet, it was so quiet compared to the beehive of activity that encapsulated their lives in spring and summer. She looked out through the window at the softly falling snow, which rested on the trees: apple, cherry, pear—their main source of income for years to come. Still, re-

---

*spider- frying pan, skillet. Cast iron, noted for three legs that held it up over cooking stove fire, giving the appearance of an arachnid. The "Erie" brand also bore a spider in a web logo on the bottom.

cently, Clarence had talked of branching out by starting a trucking concern, an obvious outgrowth of their current business as he had built up many connections while hauling apples and other fruits to New York.

If Clarence didn't trim the trees today, he would instead make the snowy trek out to chop down the stand of trees on the property he rented nearby. The timber produced firewood, not only for their own home, but brought in an extra means of income since they sold the excess to other farmers. Especially in the winter, that helped to supplement the money Clarence got for fruit. The packing house was near full to the brim with apples, as the harvest had only ended a couple of months ago. But on the farm, even if you'd had a good year—even if you'd avoided the hailstorms and there was enough money to buy the insecticide spray for the spray-rig and even if the warm days and cool nights in the Fall had produced a bumper crop of apples—you always had to worry a little about the money. When would it come in, and would it ever be enough?

Edna's eye fell on her household accounts list, which sat there on the kitchen table, accusingly. Managing the household finances had proven to be more of a challenge than she had expected. Ma and Pa had run a frugal home, always saving scraps of string, cloth, and paper, conserving precious water, so she knew how to make economies. But it seemed that since she married, all sorts of expenses barged into their lives when they least expected—or were prepared for—them. Yet, all of them were necessities and Clarence agreed they must be acquired. Still, they came to sixteen dollars this month! That was definitely beyond the budget she and Clarence had agreed upon.

Household list

Mattrass Springs $10.70
2 Shirts 2.50
Shoes 2.00
Eunice 1.00
Dr. 1.25

You tried to save, of course, as she'd read about in *"The Rural New Yorker"*. And Ma and her sisters gave Edna plenty of tips on how to stretch baking and cooking supplies, how to mend and sew what seemed to be thoroughly threadbare, how to save lard and bacon grease for later use. She smiled to herself, remembering a time when she was young, and had received an unexpected monetary "windfall" due to the largesse of a famous and wealthy man. Edna, Jennie, Chauncey and Stanley had been sitting on the stone wall that ringed the perimeter of their property, across the street from the impressive Rockefeller home, where quite a commotion was underway on this particular day. Sure enough, a man who seemed to be trailed by several "hangers-on," spied the four children observing the "show" from across the road. He turned his head and spotted the children and suddenly, to their surprise, he broke from the crowd gathered around him, crossed the road and came to greet them! As he approached, he dug his hand into his deep pockets, and pulled out shiny coins that glinted in the afternoon sun. One by one, he solemnly handed each child a glittering new dime, admonishing them to spend it wisely or better yet, to save it for the future. Later on, Ma and Pa pulled the kids aside and said, "Don't you know who that was? Why that was Old John D. Rockefeller!" At the time, the gravity of the encounter with the famous industrialist and founder of the Standard Oil Company, was lost on the children. Edna couldn't remember what she had done with her dime. Probably she and her siblings had run off to the nearby General Store to buy candy or some foolish thing. If only she still had that shiny dime right now! Well, as Ma always said, "The Lord will provide." And He always did.

No more woolgathering, Edna thought, as she turned the pages, looking for gingerbread. This was one she had wanted to try. It was written by a young New England man who wanted the readers of *"The Rural New Yorker"* to know that yes, "boys can cook as well as girls..."

Mother's Gingerbread:

To ½ cup sugar, one cup molasses and ½ teaspoon of salt, add ½ cup melted lard, stirring in well. Then in half a cup of boiling water dissolve ½ teaspoon baking soda. Add this to the rest. Don't forget one teaspoon ginger. Last but not least comes the flour, two cups sifted fine. The mixture must now be stirred vigorously for several minutes so as to get out all the lumps. Pour in a well-greased pan and bake in a moderate oven. Sour milk can be substituted for water and an egg can also be used. Yours for gingerbread, Skinny, New Hampshire.*

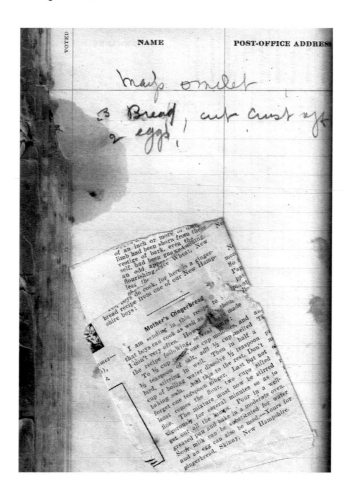

---

*Believed to be from "The Rural New Yorker"- unknown date

Recipe for Crullers

    2 eggs
    1 cup milk
    1 cup sugar
    3 cup of flour
    1 teaspoonful salt
    1 tablespoonful butter
    3 teaspoonful of baking powder.

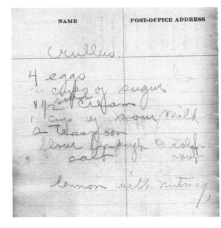

Mix well until stiff enough to roll. Add more flour if necessary.

(Note: these would have been deep fried in oil or lard until golden brown—the equivalent of modern day doughnuts)

Recipe for "Lottie's Hot Waffles"

    4 eggs (beat lightly)
    put in 1 ¾ cup of sugar and beat again
    2 cups flour
    2 teaspoons of Baking powder
    salt and flavoring
    Then the last put in ¾ of a cup of boiling water

(Note: Presumably, this mixture would then be poured onto a pre-heated, greased griddle and cooked until browned)

Cast Iron Stove, April 2006

Like my Grandmother, I moved into a farmhouse shortly after marrying. Our home began its existence as a "shotgun-style" bungalow back in the 1920s (so named because the rooms were set out in a straight line from front to back, allowing anyone—should they be so inclined—to pick off a shot with their firearm and have the bullet sail directly from one end of the house to the other). Among its many charms, we found, sitting squatly in the basement of our new (old) home, was a marvelously huge piece of history: a cast-iron woodstove, surely of the genus once employed by my grandmother and great-aunts, undoubtedly carrying with it all the attendant difficulties in getting it lit and fired up to an appropriate temperature for the day's cooking and baking. Having been used to late-20th and early-21st century electronics I wondered, "What must it have been like to use one of these? Had I lived then, how successful might I have been in wrestling with this particular appliance on a daily basis?"

The "Mighty Oakland Duplex B," as I dubbed it, had sat unused for years. It is a lovely shade of battleship-gray, constructed of sturdy cast-iron, intended to be fired by wood, much as those used by my long-ago relatives. On the top surface, one burner was designed with openwork curlicues, far prettier than the industrial-looking electric heating coils atop the 1950s stove I grew up with. The remaining burners had flat round covers that resembled mini-manholes, each slotted with a small square opening by which the lady of the house might insert a long metal crowbar for their safe removal when too hot to handle.

This was a no-fooling, several-hundred- pound behemoth of cookery. And as a historic relic, it was most intriguing. I peered closer in the dim light to see that the Oakland Duplex B had been manufactured in North Dighton, Massachusetts. The patent information on the front reads "October 24, 1922." Wow. Smack in the time period when my own grandmother would have just been setting up her home. Now this was a find!

I remembered the story told to me by the previous owner when we bought the house. Taking her turn as caretaker of the property, she had bought it from its mid-20th century owners, whose impossibly romantic names were Mabel and Walter Love. Monikers right out of a novel! She explained that even when Mabel had acquired a more up-to-date stove in the kitchen on the first floor, for years she continued to descend into the basement to stir up all her jams and jellies. Old habits die hard, and for that task, nothing would do but the old "Oakland Duplex B," which was vented through an ancient brick chimney, original to the house, and still standing.

"Hey," I said to my husband, an idea growing in my mind and gathering steam by the minute. "We could use this old wood stove any time the power goes out. I could cook up meals and do some baking…how cool would that be?"

"No!" shouted the home inspector, startling us, as we'd nearly forgotten he was there with us in the basement, checking out the vital signs on the furnace.

"But why not?" I asked.

"If you want to burn your house down to the ground, then go ahead and use that old stove. It's unbelievably dangerous!" he barked, yanking me out of my reverie with a stern warning that under no circumstances should we *ever* try to duplicate Mabel's efforts with the stove or risk imminent fire. The old chimney it was connected to was just too old, and too unsafe to attempt it.

"Sure would have been fun to try it, though," I grumbled, not wanting to give up the dream. Still, we had moved heaven and earth to get into the house; the last thing I needed to do was to torch it in a pigheaded attempt to recreate history. Not that I really would have had the know-how to get it started in the first place. So, by virtue of its elephantine weight, and our inability to even contemplate what it would take to move such a monster, we have left the stove content in its resting place, where I like to think it serves as a sort of culinary totem, imparting ancient cooking vibes that waft upstairs to flavor my own current-day concoctions.

Compensating for my lost opportunity, instead I use the "central casting" of my imagination to form a picture of Mabel (which may or may not bear any actual resemblance to the woman), drawing up a portrait of the consummate homemaker of her era: slightly plump, with silver hair, pink-cheeks-and-powder visage, tying on a clean apron, bustling about on a day filled with jam-making endeavors, kettle of soup bubbling on the range, setting aside time to sew a fine seam or darn some socks while never forgetting to keep the tidy house spic-and-span immaculate.

I am told the Loves delighted in stirring up steaming hot cups of cocoa for the neighborhood children in winter and I can happily conjure up thoughts of them, solicitously preparing the chocolaty cups of goodness, beaming while looking out the back door as the kids tobogganed down the steep snow-covered hill behind our house, peals of laughter, thrills and spills mixing together in the cold, crisp air.

Spring, 1923

Edna ran the final seam down the blue velvet curtain, pulled the material away from the sewing machine and held up the curtains to see her handiwork. Navy blue velvet would look so elegant framing our parlor windows, she thought, especially paired with the plush gold carpeting, adorned with a pattern of scarlet cabbage roses. The gold carpeting matched the amber color candlesticks and companion serving bowl she had placed on the table nearby. When she had received them as a wedding gift, she had wondered when, as a farm wife, she might have a dinner or gathering so elegant as to necessitate employing such lovely items? But it was reassuring to have them there; a touch of sophistication to remind her that while day-to-day life might feel like drudgery at times, there were finer things to which she could aspire. Maybe a fancy wedding of her own children, one day?

"Humph!" sniffed Carrie when Edna had shown her the velvet material she'd procured from her sister Jessie's brother-in-law in New York City. "Not what I'd choose at all. And how much did it cost? I'm sure it was too dear* for Clarence's budget," said Carrie coldly. My, she was eternally peevish, thought Edna, as she smoothed out the seams of the curtains. Carrie's mouth was always set, hard and forbidding, chin jutting out, as if challenging Edna to defend anything she did or said. Her mother-in-law had not softened one iota in the two years since Clarence and Edna had married, even with the advent of little Esther, her first and only grandchild. Edna felt the better part of valor was to remain quiet whenever Carrie found fault, and Edna became adept at quickly

---

*dear- expensive

changing the subject. Thankfully, Carrie's visits to the other side of the house were brief—she burst in, said her piece, and as if summoned by an unseen caller, turned abruptly on her heel, and marched back to her own quarters. This time was no different, and Edna couldn't help but be relieved. Thank goodness she didn't have to share the house, the kitchen, the decorating decisions with Carrie Yager. Nothing was good enough for that woman, and no other opinion would be tolerated. Life was not something to be enjoyed or celebrated for Carrie. Oh, no. For Carrie, marking out the days of a life were like doing the dishes: a bleak chore to be endured, completed, put away in proper order, then recommenced in the next 24 hour cycle.

Edna and Esther

In the kitchen, little Esther sat on a blanket on the floor, clutching a spoon in one chubby fist and a block in the other, banging the cube at intervals on the floor. The child giggled at the commotion she made, apparently unmoved by the grim mood imparted by her grandmother's visit.

It was already past time to start Clarence's dinner, but Edna had been so engrossed she kept thinking, "Just five minutes more," with the draperies. While he didn't rhapsodize about most food (other than the fruits he grew), no doubt he would be hungry and eager to dig into hearty Scalloped Beef tonight.

Scalloped Beef
1 layer of beef
1 layer of onions
1 layer of potatoes
salt and pepper
1 ½ of suet (same as scalloped salmon)
I take ground steak.

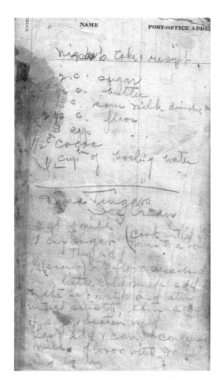

Nina's Cake Receipt

Tomorrow's festivities loomed as well and she would need to bake a couple of items. Edna temporarily abandoned the home decorations and went to the kitchen, pulled out her recipe book and leafed through the possibilities until she found "Nina's Cake receipt"

Nina's Cake Receipt
2 cups sugar
½ cup butter
1 cup sour milk dissolved one teaspoon soda
2 1/3 cup flour
3 eggs
½ cup cocoa
1 /2 cup boiling water

(Note: the above would have been mixed together, turned into a greased and floured pan and baked in a "moderate" oven, about 350 degrees)

This was only the first of two cakes she planned to make. As she cracked the eggs into the bowl, and stirred them up, her mind went back to Carrie's unnecessary criticism. Well, she was wrong! Edna thought defiantly. She was proud that the hand-made curtains had turned out admirably well, given that her sister Jennie was the real seamstress in the family. For her part, Edna's skills lay in cooking and baking. She was never so comfortable as she was in the kitchen, stirring up breakfast, lunch and dinner. Likewise for her sisters Blanche and Jessie. They shared recipes all around among the family and with neighbor and church friends; each gave the other full credit in their recipe books, duly citing at the heading of each page: "Mrs. Stanley Coons's White Cake," or "Edna's Crullers," or "Pickle (Mrs. Barringer)".

Fancy cakes were most often made for church events, which is exactly what her baking was intended for today. Years ago at home, Ma and Pa would set a fine table for the occasional card game but of course now, since her wedding, card games at her own home were, as the German folks often said, strictly *verboten*. Clarence was dead-set against card playing in any shape or form.

"Card playing is gambling, plain and simple," Clarence pronounced grimly one night when Edna originally broached the subject.

"But Clarence, we don't play for money, "Edna protested, "It's just a game."

"Games are for children, Edna," said Clarence, "I won't have it in my house. Remember who we are." He pronounced it like a king, reminding the nobles they had to set an example. The Yagers were proud folk, and felt they had a reputation to uphold as defenders of correct behavior, staunch supporters of God and Right over Wrong.

Not that she really missed the *activity* of the playing, but she sometimes did miss the lively chatter that accompanied it, the roars at an excellently played hand, the teasing over the poorly executed gambit. Still, in her short three years of marriage thus far, she had learned that Clarence could be hard-headed about certain things that her own family felt were simply "having fun". Best not to make waves, as it was a small matter. And Clarence didn't deny her the opportunity to join in card playing at Ma's or other folks' houses. She smiled, thinking about all this fuss over gambling. Goodness knows her relatives were such penny-pinchers anyway, they couldn't imagine wasting money on a mere game! But in order to keep the peace at home, she declined any card-party offers.

Tomorrow's gathering was certainly sanctioned by the Yagers— a church bake sale. Early in the morning, Edna planned to get up and make Mrs. Harders Angles Cake (sic), a real extravagance as it called for the whites of 11 eggs, which was a lot to sink into one little cake! That near-dozen could otherwise have been earmarked for sale to locals who didn't have their own chickens. Sometimes, collecting a dozen fresh eggs could be a real feat. Over the years, Edna had come up with a tried-and-true method; first, she would strew feed for the hens just out of reach of their nests, which lured them to abandon their post temporarily in search of breakfast. In theory, that would give Edna time to snatch up the eggs, while the hens were distracted with gobbling up the kernels. But it wasn't always that simple. Occasionally a brooder would hold her ground on the nest and sharp pecks would rain down on Edna's hand as she reached under the sitting hen to pluck her prize. You had to approach gently, inserting your hand under the warm feathery bosom, encase the egg with your fingers like a cage, taking care to protect them as you withdrew slowly. It was important to steel yourself against a possible hen attack, so that you didn't inadvertently crush the egg in a reflexive response to the hen's beaky assault. Still, it was worth the trouble. There was hardly a soul who hadn't bitten into the dreamy cloud that was Mrs. Harder's cake—light, fluffy, as if eating a soufflé—and didn't sigh in delight, then beg for the recipe.

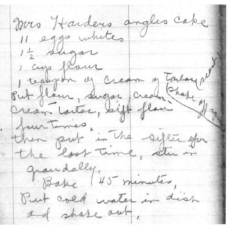

Mrs. Harder's Angles (angel) Cake

Mrs. Harders Angles (sic) Cake

    11 egg whites
    1 ½ cup sugar
    1 cup flour
    1 teaspoon cream of tartar (scant, shake off spoon)

Put flour, sugar, cream tartar together, sift flour four times. Then put in the sifter for the last time, stir in gradually. Bake 45 minutes. Put cold water in dish and shake out.

Edna checked the fire to see that the oven was "moderate" for Nina's cake. She greased and floured two pans and poured in the batter. No bubbles, everything looked smooth and silky. She popped the pans in the oven and made a mental note of the time on the wall clock. The frosting would have to wait until the cakes were taken out and cooled. This particular cake, beloved by her husband's own grandmother, made her think of the oft-told family tale of a party for some of the ladies of the town that his grandmother had given in the mid-1800s. Clarence's Grandmother Margaret—so unlike Carrie, the current matriarch in this house—liked to have a good laugh whenever she got the chance. In his work as a tug boat engineer on the Hudson, Clarence's Grandfather Jacob made daily trips down to New York City and then back home. He often surprised his family by bringing back "the latest thing"—what style dictated as the current custom amongst the "high-toned" denizens of the metropolis, and a source of no small wonder for rural upstate citizens. No end of new and delightful trinkets were tucked into his pocket before he headed home, and were produced with a flourish, for the family and invited guests to admire and remark upon. The most recent gewgaw he had plucked from the sophisticated streets of New York were called toothpicks, a new-fangled marvel of post-meal dental aids and, as it turned out, entertainment. Who, in the farm circles of Germantown, had ever seen such a thing?

"Let's just see what they say!" Margaret said, as she decided to add these so-called toothpicks to the array already laid out for a special ladies' luncheon she was holding the next day. Alongside the table groaning with frosted layer cakes, meringue-cloud lemon pies, molasses cakes, coffee, tea, and sugar supported by her finest table linens, good china and silverware, she set out the small wooden sticks in a diminutive blue, cut-glass container shaped in the form of a top hat.

When the ladies arrived in their Sunday best, the visitors were ushered into the parlor where they spotted the unusual offering. All eyes were drawn to the blue container on the table. Why was it holding what

Margaret Yager, Clarence's grandmother

resembled filed-down matchsticks on the table? They looked at each other quizzically and then back at the contents of the small top hat, as they had surely never seen such a thing in all their lives, but each one feared looking foolish by asking their hostess, "What *are* they?" And who among them didn't want to partake of what was *a la mode* among those in the know?

Clarence's grandmother told the ladies to help themselves to whatever they desired. Suppressing a laugh at their bewilderment, she listened for murmurs as she ducked back to the kitchen to get cream for the tea. When she returned to inquire "Has everyone had tea, coffee, cake?" she entered the room to find six very serious ladies, politely and contemplatively *eating* the toothpicks proffered by their hosts.

Candlesticks, June 2010

"You want that? It's your grandmother's!" pronounced my Aunt Winnie as we settled into a cozy booth in a restaurant with my mother, and my cousin Cathy. From her voluminous purse, Winnie produced a squat, amber-colored glass candlestick with some bits of white wax still clinging to the sides, and placed it triumphantly before me. I ran my finger around the bottom where some delicate flowers resembling daisies were etched, winding around the base, trailed by long, thin stems sporting leaves. Turning it over in my hands, I tried to come up with something to say. It was nothing that knocked my socks off. It was the kind of thing you saw in many senior ladies' collections, and was usually offered when they got tired of dusting around these tchotchkes day in and day out. My husband and I had seen countless examples of the same sort at auctions, the detritus of years of handed-down family acquisitions, passed on in hopes that someone in the next generation might treasure it.

My Aunt explained that the candlestick's twin, plus a matching serving dish, with a wide channel for displaying comestibles, was waiting for me in the car. I could see that the candlestick's base was not perfectly round—it had a slightly lopsided circumference, leading me to wonder if it had been hand-blown back in the 1920s? No doubt it was a wedding gift for my Grandma Edna, or perhaps something she purchased when a new bride. Amber would match our bungalow décor, but I already had an ample supply of candlesticks, including a beautiful crystal pair we'd received as a wedding gift…so why did I need another set?

I appealed to my very sensible cousin. "Don't you want them?" I pleaded. She rolled her eyes, dismissing the thought with a wave of her hand and said, "NO, thanks!" She had recently begun a household purge of items she didn't particularly care about or found to be less than utilitarian, hoping to avoid that same "little old lady syndrome" of becoming a warehouse for excess useless items, when we reached our dotage.

"OK," I said hesitantly, not fully convinced I wanted or needed these items. I set the candlestick aside, thinking I could easily tuck it away into my handbag when we left the restaurant. So, we turned to new thoughts, new conversations. An hour later, in the distraction of bill-paying and gathering up our doggie bags, I had a vague notion in the back of my mind about the candlestick, believing I had already stowed it in my purse. Getting back outside to my cousin's car, I saw her reaching in the hatchback to retrieve the second candlestick and matching dish. I took it, we bundled our respective mothers into our cars, said our goodbyes and drove in separate directions.

Three hours and a 170-mile round-trip later, I arrived home and it occurred to me to search my purse for the first candlestick. Not there. The other stick and the large dish were in the back seat. Surely I hadn't been so stupid as to have left it behind on the restaurant table, next to the ketchup bottle and coffee creamer? Worse yet, would I really have to go all the way back to retrieve it? Maybe this was the action equivalent of a Freudian slip ("Oh dear, did I leave that *behind*?"), since I had been an initially reluctant recipient. Honestly, did I *really* want it?

Still (I argued with myself) it *was* a family heirloom, whether I found it appealing or not. Surely, out of deference to my aunt, and in thanks for her kindness in sharing it with me, I should see what I could do to get it back? Fearing it might already have been discarded with the restaurant garbage or even pocketed by a subsequent diner, I looked up the phone number and called the establishment. Success! Minutes after our departure, our waitress had spotted and corralled the candlestick, and promised to put it away for safekeeping in the manager's office. I knew anything could happen between now and a week later when I was able to drive back and pick it up. But that next Sunday I drove the 170-mile round trip once again, only to realize when I pulled up to a shuttered restaurant that it was closed for the July 4th holiday. Driving away, disgusted with myself for not phoning first, I chided myself, "What are you doing, wasting all this gas and time, trying to get back something you never really wanted in the first place?" But then, strong feelings that I'd regret it, if I just let it go, crept into my consciousness. Somehow, if I didn't do my utmost to retrieve the candlestick, I was not only letting myself down, I was letting down my whole family—past and present.

The second attempt a week later was the charm. The restaurant was open, the boss still had the candlestick locked in his office and true to his word, produced it when I arrived. A sense of relief washed over me and I claimed the candlestick with profuse thanks to the very kind management, feeling supremely triumphant at having brought it back into the family fold. Strange, how I had become rather obsessed with having it back in my possession, given how disinterested I had been when it was first thrust into my hands. Perhaps its value was growing on me.

How many times had Grandma Edna run her finger over the etched flowers and the imperfectly "round" base of these candlesticks as I was doing at this moment? Or placed food "just so" in the bowl when entertaining company? Something had compelled me to rescue this household item that had once meant so much to Grandma Edna. Maybe, like Proust's madeleines, it wasn't the object itself, but what it *represented* that mattered. All I knew was, this was the second time in six months that a belonging of my grandmother's had pushed itself into my hands, seemingly out of nowhere. And, unaccountably, I was glad.

Chapter 5

(Pickle) Mrs. Barringer

July, 1924

"Here's yer washing," exhaled Mrs. Barringer as she laboriously hoisted the basket of freshly laundered clothes into the front door. Simply moving through life was difficult for Mrs. Barringer. Everything about her was rubbed raw and red, from her ruddy cheeks to her scrub-worn knuckles. She was a hefty woman, who looked a bit like a sack of potatoes tied in the middle, with a sprinkling of freckles across her broad face, and unruly red-brown curls that escaped every attempt at wrangling them into a hairdo.

"Oh, sit down, sit down Mrs. Barringer," Edna hastened around the table to usher her visitor into a chair. It was clear the morning's exertions had winded Mrs. Barringer, who wiped her perspiring brow with a handkerchief and futilely attempted to smooth back one of the multitudes of stray wisps of hair. Mrs. Barringer exhaled heavily and plopped down in the chair. The first day of the week was always busy for her, as she commonly picked up washing to be done by the week's end on Friday. Germantown farm lives were circumscribed by certain days of the week: Saturdays you "filed the stoop"*, Sundays were the Lord's Day, Mondays were for washing.

Edna dashed to the stove and felt the coffee pot. It was still warm and still had a little something inside. She looked at Mrs. Barringer's swollen ankles, looking like someone had inflated them with a bicycle pump minutes after she laced up her shoes. Edna felt pity for the poor woman, who trudged all over town with other people's laundry, just so she could make a living. Edna could tell Mrs. Barringer would like the excuse to sit a spell, so she asked, "Won't you stop for a bit and have some coffee?" Having extended the invitation, she belatedly made a quick mental inventory of what she had on

---

*file the stoop (clean house, scrub floors, mop, scour from the Dutch" feilen")

hand to serve Mrs. Barringer, who, in addition to stellar laundering abilities, was acknowledged by all to be a peerless cook and baker. Edna figured it was too soon to serve the custard cups she had made earlier in the morning, as they really needed time to set up. You really had to treat custard very delicately. Once you mixed up the eggs, sugar, milk and vanilla, you poured it into sturdy brown earthenware cups. Then, they were gingerly set inside a roaster pan whereupon you poured boiling hot water from a kettle all around the cups in a sort of bath. You had to take care not to splash any drops inside the cups or fail to mark the correct amount of time, or your custard would turn out watery. Once prepared, you slowly slid the roaster pan into the oven and cooked it at a moderate setting. It reminded Edna of how, when she was a girl growing up, they had to boil kettles and kettles of water to take baths on a Saturday night. With nine children plus Ma and Pa, no one wanted to be the last one in line for the water everyone else had bathed in before! And the initially scalding temperature in the tub cooled considerably as you waited for each successive kettle to finish boiling. How lucky she was that she had a modern husband who insisted on indoor plumbing!

Thankfully, Edna remembered she had some day-old molasses cakes that would complement Mrs. Barringer's cup of coffee.

"I made these molasses cakes yesterday and I'd really like to know your opinion of them," said Edna, entreating her guest to partake. Mrs. Barringer looked eagerly at the fragrant molasses cakes and seemed to revive a bit with the prospect of a tasty morsel, and seemed to revive a bit at the prospect of tucking into one or two.

"Don't mind if I do, "she said brightening significantly.

Edna got out cream and sugar and poured out two coffee cups to set on the table. She knew Mrs. Barringer's life was hard. Mrs. Barringer had married a man 20 years her senior, quickly had two children by him and just as quickly found him dead of a heart attack one morning shortly after he'd risen, dressed and was sitting reading his morning paper. Money was tight, so Mrs. Barringer took in other people's washing. She did it cheerfully, and some women like Edna, who didn't really need the help but wanted to give Mrs. Barringer a "leg up," spent what could be spared from their weekly household budgets with the conviction that not only were they saving themselves the trouble of laundering, they were also doing their part to help keep the Barringer family going. Mrs. Barringer's two boys were high-spirited, always tearing about town with grimy clothes and the same wayward curls as their Mother. No doubt Mrs. Barringer was so dog-tired after wrestling with other people's washing all day long, that she had little energy to tackle the cleanliness of her offspring. But it was clear that she loved her boys. From their pew in the back of the church, Edna had glimpsed a tender look spreading over Mrs. Barringer's face during Sunday services, as she licked her palm and patted down a wayward cowlick on her younger son's head.

"Did ya see about the Alexander Hamilton coming in to Hudson?" asked Mrs. Barringer. "Could be a great thing!" she declared optimistically, as she poured a slight drop of milk into her coffee and reached for a substantial molasses cake.

Edna knew what Mrs. Barringer was talking about. The side-wheel paddle steamer Alexander Hamilton had just been acquired by the Hudson River Day Line and was bringing up New York City residents to Hudson for daily or weekly visits at a steady clip. Mrs. Barringer was always on the lookout for a new economic prospect, hoping she might sell some of her delicious baked goods or canned conserves to the city folk. Goodness knows the extra money probably helped the poor woman to get by.

The sun streamed through the window, as yellow at the yolks of the fresh eggs Edna had unearthed this morning from the chickens, who, predictably, clucked their disapproval at being disturbed as they slumbered on toasty warm nests. That gave Edna a flash of an idea!

"Mrs. Barringer," she said, pushing the cookie plate toward her guest again, "I have extra eggs this morning, as the hens have been laying to beat the band. Would you be so kind as to take a few off my hands? They'll just go bad before I can use them up." Edna was trying to make it easy for Mrs. Barringer to say yes.

Not wanting to appear too eager, Mrs. Barringer wiped crumbs from the molasses cake off her ample bosom, and then took a slurp of coffee for good measure. These were mere distractions from the topic before she answered, although she had all she could do to stop from shouting that yes, absolutely she would love to take the eggs! She disdained those who offered charity, because she had her pride—yet she knew from past experience that Edna meant it kindly. And goodness knows a dozen eggs could help them get through to the end of the week. This past week, the laundry business had been slow and the amount she took in would barely pay for the week's groceries. And the boys had been well-behaved lately. She dearly loved surprising them with sweet treats when they came home from school though she could scarce afford to, most times. While a rare treat, custard was one of their favorites and these excess eggs that Edna had in abundance, would make some lovely custard cups for the boys. There was something so satisfying in seeing hungry children tucking into food with abandon—food you have made with them in mind. Their smiles were a sure reward for your efforts.

"Well, if you can't use them up right away..." she trailed off, giving Edna the chance to jump in and insist.

"No, honest and truly," Edna encouraged. "I'd rather you make one of your delicious cakes or custards with these eggs than to see them spoil!"

Mrs. Barringer had good reason to be wary of offers as she was looked down upon by some of the more affluent folks in town, just because she took in laundry for a living. "She looks like she was called for and couldn't come," sniffed Edna's sister Blanche, referring to the state of continual deterioration Mrs. Barringer's personal clothes and grooming had found themselves in. That was not to say that Mrs. Barringer didn't excel in her laundry skills—she got other folks' clothes squeaky clean and fresh-smelling, then starched and ironed them within an inch of their lives. But people often needed something to feel superior about, and Mrs. Barringer occasionally bore the brunt of their insecurities.

"For shame, Blanche!" said Edna reproachfully to her elder sister. If there were two things in this world she could not abide, it was unfairness and unkindness. "She's a widow who works her fingers to the bone!" Blanche, taken aback at the vehemence of the outburst and surprise that her younger sister would question her, was stunned into an uncustomary silence.

Edna liked Mrs. Barringer's cheerful spirit despite the adversity she had experienced in her life and truthfully, she enjoyed Mrs. Barringer's company. And while they might "snip" * behind her back, town ladies had to admit a grudging respect for her, because Mrs. Barringer had a remarkable talent the rest could only stand back and admire. The reason was: Mrs. Barringer had an unerring taste for the right seasoning and the best recipes. Flaky, buttery biscuits, lighter than air; silky cream pies; cinnamon-laced coffee cake; tangy-sweet bread-and-butter pickles—her kitchen turned them all out with nary a mistake. Few of the town ladies had cookbooks that didn't contain one of Mrs. Barringer's recipes. Where did she find them all? Did she make them up after experimenting all night in her kitchen? Her value as a judge of fine cooking was without parallel. It was common for women, at least in the privacy of their own homes where others wouldn't judge them, to ask her to critique something new they had attempted, seeking her opinion.

"Just taste these scalloped potatoes and see what you think," they'd plead, as Mrs. Barringer took the spoon, consumed its contents, gave it a thoughtful once-over, smacked her lips a minute or two and formed her assessment: "Just add a half-spoonful more of salt," she'd diagnose, like a doctor prescribing for an ailment. Or: "A little more butter and a little less flour, I think," giving it the full weight of her diligent consideration. Consequently, even the sniffy ladies in town secretly held her in some esteem for her capabilities. And it was her recipe for pickles that just about every cook in town most coveted.

One of Mrs. Barringer's many recipes, courtesy of Aunt Blanche's recipe book

---

*snip- to gossip, to be "snippy" about someone or something

Pickle (Mrs. Barringer's)

1 head cabbage

5 red peppers

4 quarts green tomatoes

4 onions

Sauce: 2 pounds brown sugar

3 teaspoons celery seed

3 teaspoons salt

¾ pint vinegar

1 teaspoon turmeric

Cook all together then thicken with flour

(Note: the first 4 ingredients would have been cooked in the sauce until the ingredients melded, then set aside to cool in the refrigerator. They would be served as a relish.

Mother's Molasses Cakes
(as it appears in Edna's recipe book)

1 cup of molasses

1 cup of sugar

1 cup buttermilk

½ cup butter

2 eggs

2 teaspoonfuls soda

1 tablespoonful cinnamon

3 cups of flour

pinch of salt

Edna's recipe for Mother's
Molasses Cakes

Gramma Coons Molasses Cookies (For modern cooks)

(original recipe handed down through the family, updated for modern cooks with temperature and time)

>   1 cup sugar
>   1 cup light molasses
>   1 cup lard (Crisco or other shortening)
>   Add 2 unbeaten eggs. Stir until well mixed.
>   Stir:
>   2 teaspoons baking soda into 8 tablespoons boiling water.

While this bubbles, pour it into mixture in bowl.

Add: 1 teaspoon cinnamon
>   2 teaspoons ginger
>   1 teaspoon salt

Sift into another bowl:
>   5 cups flour
>   2 teaspoons baking powder

(Note: The original recipe says "Let stand a half day." There is no need for this, they may be baked right away if you desire.)

Drop by spoon onto slightly greased cookie sheets. Bake at 350 degrees for 10-12 minutes.

Aunt Jennie Coons' Custard (For Modern Cooks)

(Updated for modern cooks with temperature and time)

>   2 cups milk, scalded
>   ¼ cup sugar
>   2 eggs, lightly beaten
>   1 teaspoon vanilla
>   pinch salt

Mix above ingredients and pour into custard cups. Sprinkle with nutmeg if desired, or flakes of coconut. Place in baking pan and pour boiling hot water to come halfway up the cups. Bake at 350 degrees. Use a silver knife to test after 15 minutes. If knife comes out clean (about 20 minutes' time) remove from oven. Chill in refrigerator.

Homemade Toilet Soap*

The following formula for making toilet soap is given, in response to a number of requests, by Miss Gladys Bradley, extension worker in home economics for Garfield County, Colo:

> Five pounds fat (three of tallow and two of lard is a good proportion. All of either kind may be used. Mutton tallow is excellent too.)
>
> One can lye.
>
> Two and one-half pints cold water
>
> Four tablespoons borax
>
> Three tablespoons glycerine
>
> One ounce citronella (oil of rose geranium or lavender is good)
>
> Coloring if desired (chlorophyll makes a good green)

Melt fat and cool to 100 to 110 degrees. Dissolve lye in the cold water (do not use an aluminum container) and cool to 80 to 85 degrees. The borax may be dissolved in the lye solution also.

Pour lye solution in a slow, steady stream into fat, stirring with an even, steady motion. Too vigorous beating will cause the soap to separate. Add glycerine, coloring and scent. When a honey-like texture is formed pour into a mold. Cover with a blanket and keep in a warm room for 24 hours. Cut and store in a cool place. Do not allow to freeze. Tar soap may be made by adding eight ounces of tar when the soap begins to thicken."

---

*From Aunt Blanche's recipe book—unknown provenance

Eggs, Spring 2008

Is there anything more satisfying on a rainy Sunday morning than making a plate of scrambled eggs, with my dogs looking on in eager anticipation of sharing the feast? If there is, it doesn't come to mind. There is something primally satisfying about eggs, even though it seems this dietary staple goes in and out of favor from generation to generation.

I see two big pairs of eyes in upturned, furry faces, looking at me pleadingly. Like many in my Baby Boom generation who are childless, I see my dogs as child "surrogates," and cooking for the family includes cooking for them, without reservation. Cole, an endearing black-and-white male Siberian Husky, is the first into the kitchen when he hears the sounds of egg cracking against glass bowl. Sophie, our silver-gray bouncy female husky, bounds in, only to flop down immediately to secure her spot next to the counter, as they wait. Few preparations of meals go without the oversight of our pups, who perform their work as diligently as any factory inspector. Cereal is the workaday solution to my need for morning nutrition—that's fine for the Monday-through-Saturday treadmill. But when Sunday rolls around, I opt for the less Spartan, supremely tasty scrambled eggs with cheddar cheese shavings (freely dispensed, it must be admitted, to the pups as I cut and crumble them into the eggs mixed with milk). While the fry pan heats up, I go outdoors in my purple polka dot robe and snip fresh chives from my own garden. The chives, along with a bumper crop of mint, are part of the bounty that came with this property and they reappear each spring with the same frequency that the swallows return to Capistrano. Back in the kitchen, I melt a tiny pat of butter and watch it sizzle, foam and subside. I dump the whisked golden eggy mixture, flecked with savory green chives, into the pan on moderate heat and bat the mixture around with the spatula until it's ready, crispy brown bits clinging to the sides of the pan, pepper and salt it to taste and turn it out on the dish. Two small pieces of toast bracket the plate, one of which I cover with the remains of a jar of raspberry jam and the other with sugar-and-cinnamon mix that I've combined in an old-fashioned metal shaker with big holes in its top. That reminds my of my father and the surgical precision with which he prepared his breakfast cinnamon toast, butter oozing into its rough, nubby surfaces, coated by the sugary topping. He neatly dispensed it with precise shakes, one-two-three, turn-two-three. When he was done, the entire surface was neatly covered with what looked like sweet brown sand, never any spillage, no stray grains falling to the table top, just pure unadulterated comfort food.

Plate ready, I sit down with my four-legged bookends, who eagerly stand at attention, licking their chops in anticipation. First, my portion, and then the patient dogs mop up the remains, their tongues greedily circumnavigating the plate until it is clean as a whistle. All three of us share in the feast, devouring every crumb. To put a plate of food, made by your own hand, in front of creatures you love dearly, and to see them enjoying it, is one of the sweet, fleeting pleasures of life, in my estimation.

Winter, 1925

Edna churned the egg beaters as fast as she possibly could; her right arm was fatigued and achy with the effort. Anything to drown out The Sound.

The Sound. The Sound.

It was butchering day—a time Edna met with dread. Tenderhearted as she was, she couldn't bear the thought of animals, some of whom she had an emotional attachment to, being slaughtered. But that's just the way it was on the farm. The family had to lay stores by for the cold, hard winter they'd just entered.

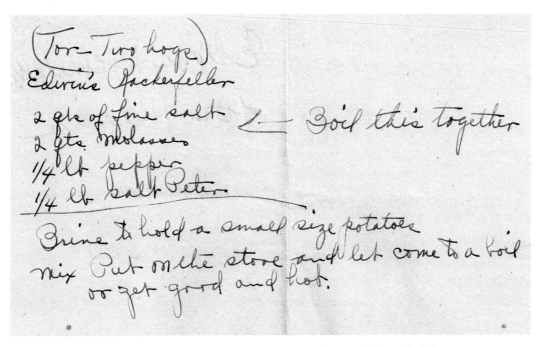

Blanche's recipe for newly butchered hogs from Edwin Rockefeller

More anguished squeals from down in the barn. The butchering continued. The worst thing about it was it was so deceptively cruel to lure these trusting little animals, who approached without fear, only to be dealt a lethal blow by those who had done nothing but feed and nurture them prior to this day. The farmers coaxed the pigs out by tickling them under the chin, which the animals just loved. The blissful pig couldn't know that a second later, a shaft of cold, sharp steel would be plunged into his hide. Edna took small comfort in thinking that the pig's very last moments—as he was being tickled under the chin—might have been happy ones. But really, what a brutal, horrible way to go. These were the animals she threw grain to every morning as she addressed them by pet names: Jane, Olive, Arthur. Luckily, sentimental farm families who might have lost their nerve having to perform this duty on their own, were aided by a man from town who arrived like clockwork each year to do the deadly deed of sticking the pigs. Still—at least in Edna's heart—hiring someone to do the worst of it, did not absolve the family of their "crimes" against these unsuspecting beasts.

Yet, Edna couldn't deny, once the sounds of butchering day had faded away and the small midsection of the pig they called the "tenderloin" was brought up to the kitchen for dinner, fried up and served with potatoes and beans, it was something amazingly delicious. How to explain the conflict she felt inside? She was at once guilty for savoring the taste of something that had until this morning been running around on its four hooves, oblivious to its impending fate. And yet, the flavor was tasty, unlike anything else.

Edna shuddered, hearing yet another squeal, and prayed it would be over soon, for her *and* the hogs.

She turned to the recipe for preparing hogs that she'd tucked away in her cookbook—thanks to her sister Blanche, who unlike Edna, had no problem with dispatching farm animals for supper.

Edna with neighbor
Eddie Rockefeller

Recipe "For Two Hogs"

  Edwins Rockefeller

  2 qts of fine salt

  2 qts molasses   *----Boil this together*

  ¼ lb pepper

  ¼ lb salt Peter

Brine to hold a small size potatoes. Mix. Put on the stove and let come to a boil or get good and hot.

Fattening Broilers

To bring good prices, cockerels must be in good flesh. Cockerels reared on a good starting and growing ration, with an abundance of grain, during the latter part of this period, usually show good flesh and yellow color. If broilers are confined and a fattening mash is desired, the following may be used:

100 lbs. yellow corn meal	50 lbs. ground oatmeal
50 lbs. middlings	30 lbs. meatscrap

If milk is available for mixing the mash, the meatscrap may be omitted. This should be fed as a wet mash three times per day, with all the cracked corn the birds will eat the last thing at night. Milk or water to drink, or both, should be provided. The temperature has a lot to do with satisfactory fattening conditions. Cool, well ventilated rooms are necessary during hot weather.

Blanche's directions for plumping up chickens

Stout Blanche, with her no-nonsense attitude to the practicalities of life on the farm, had grown adept at killing chickens, which were a staple of their diet. After following the newspaper directions for "Fattening Broilers" for the appropriate number of months, when the time came for cooking them, Blanche would simply grab a chicken by its neck with her beefy arms, deftly kill it, pluck it and set it aside, looking for her next victim.

Fattening Broilers*

"To bring good prices, cockerels must be in good flesh. Cockerels reared on a good starting and growing ration, with an abundance of grain, during the latter part of this period, usually show good flesh and yellow color. If broilers are confined and a fattening mash is desired, the following may be used:

  100 lbs. yellow corn meal

  50 lbs. middlings

  50 lbs. ground oatmeal

  30 lbs. meatscrap

---

*From Aunt Blanche's recipe book-unknown provenance

If milk is available for mixing the mash, the meatscrap may be omitted. This should be fed as a wet mash three times per day, with all the cracked corn the birds will eat the last thing at night.

Pull yourself together, thought Edna, and stop thinking about the pigs. No question, there were worse dilemmas than having to listen to The Sound, while standing in a warm, cozy kitchen. By contrast, this time of year down by the Hudson River, Abram Rockefeller's team of men who worked at "Rockefeller & Co." were bound to endure the freezing cold, hewing out huge chunks of ice with their saws. They harvested the thick blocks in bitter temperatures, to be laid up in the ice houses along the river banks. Ultimately, the ice would be used by small local households like this farm, but more importantly, the bulk of it would be preserved in sawdust or hay, so the blocks might be shipped down to New York City customers. There, restaurants, hotels and housewives could employ upstate river ice to chill their creams and custards in their own iceboxes. Ice cutting had become a major industry in the latter part of the last century, on both sides of the Hudson River. Over in West Camp, directly across the river from Germantown (Germantown was originally known as East Camp when settled by the early Palatines), the ice harvesting business was a major trade, mirroring that in their own town. Still, Clarence said recently that perhaps this vital venture might soon melt away, like the product itself. The papers were already talking about the advent of electric-run iceboxes to refrigerate food—so where would that leave the thousands who carved out their winter cash reserves on the shores of their most vital resource? Customs and ways of making a living were changing as the world kept turning. But surely, thought Edna, agriculture, as practiced by the Coons and the Yager families, would be a viable industry that would always support New York State and the rest of this country?

Well, in due course, those matters would take care of themselves—but supper would not, unless Edna put her mind to it! "Lemon Pie Without Cooking" was where her finger had fallen as she thumbed through the recipe book, planning for a hearty meal after a long-drawn out day of butchering. Surely, not needing to cook the pie filling was a time-saver, but she still had to dress up the presentation, by beating up egg whites for a fluffy meringue cloud to blanket the top of the pie. When the peaks were beaten to just the right stiffness, she put large dollops all around the pie, made sure she sealed the gap between crust and meringue, and then checked the oven. Nice and hot, just right to set up the meringue.

She had just popped the pie in when she heard the handle turn on the door that separated them from Carrie and Abram's quarters. Of course, Carrie would never do them the courtesy of knocking. In Carrie's mind, this was still her house and Clarence, Edna and little Esther were merely boarders. Of all times for her to show up, Edna thought, when I have to pay attention to my evening meal, all of a sudden here's Carrie with who-knows-what crazy idea?

"Here," Carrie said, looking like a thundercloud as she roughly shoved a battered tin pan at Edna. "We've got extra. You can have them for your supper."

Edna had quickly learned to be *feest** of any offerings that Carrie brought to the other side of the house. Already, she could smell a distinctively sour scent emanating from the pan, indicating food that was somewhat "off". Thank goodness her stomach was stronger now, having put the early nauseous stage of pregnancy behind her. Their second child was expected in just a few months now. Peeking under the dishtowel, she had to refrain from inhaling, as the putrid scent turned out to be only half of the picture. Carrie's contribution to their nighttime meal was a mound of bluish-green, clearly moldy potatoes festering in the pan, suitable only for the scrap heap but being tendered as if for Mrs. Astor's supper!

Carrie glared at Edna disapprovingly for another minute, apparently expecting some expression of gratitude, but receiving none, turned on her heel and huffed out of the room, leaving a cloud of ill will lingering behind her.

---

feest (or feast) from the Dutch, meaning disgusted with, made nauseous by, nauseated as in, "I'm feest of it".
Also *afease* -Dictionary of American Regional English

Edna stared at the potatoes for a good minute, when uncontrollable giggles started to rise up in her throat, hard as she tried to stifle them. What could she possibly do with this mess? If she tossed it out with the kitchen slop, Carrie would certainly see and trouble would ensue. While other daughters-in-law would be aggrieved and put-upon, really, this was just too comical for words and Edna could only imagine what Ma and her family would say when she told them!

Edna glanced up at the clock. 3 pm. Although it was January, it was a crystal clear day and the roads would be open. The lemon meringue pie would only take a few more minutes. While it cooled on the counter, surely there was time to run over to Ma's just to show her the ludicrous "gift" she'd received? Better yet, she could ditch the potatoes in Ma's kitchen slop and Carrie would be none the wiser. Edna laughed out loud at the thought. No matter how long she lived in her current home with Clarence, she would always feel like something of a "tenant" in the Yager house. Without question, they had their six rooms, separate from Carrie and Abram, but it was always clear that they resided there at the pleasure of her in-laws, not as full owners of their half of the house. Going to Ma's was a treat, because the kitchen was always warm and busy, conversation bubbled over, like the pots on the stove, and a good laugh restored the soul. Yes, even for a few minutes, familial time was just what Edna needed.

Edna pulled the steaming pie out of the stove and set it on the counter to cool, bundled up Esther and jumped in the Marmon to head over to Ma's. She always felt proud and particularly up-to-date when she got into her sleek Marmon car. Clarence was surprisingly enlightened in his attitudes toward women driving, and was the instigator in her tutelage in motoring, first teaching Edna how to drive, and then buying her this beautiful automobile. The man did like his auto cars! She remembered the newspaper advertisement of a stylish woman in a cloche hat, depressing the clutch of a Marmon with her fashionably-shod foot. Every time Edna got into the car, she felt a little of that smart looking woman rubbed off on her, even though the demands of her daily routine as a farm wife meant that attempts at style and sophistication were a rare and often frivolous consideration.

It took only a matter of minutes to pull up to Ma's kitchen door and Edna pulled up the parking brake to hold the car in place. With baby Esther on one arm, she scooped up her "gift" from Carrie in the other hand, and hurried to the warmth of a busy kitchen, full of the kinetic energy of a large family, jostling around each other as they prepared for the evening meal, surrounded by welcoming bright lights and delicious smells that all but reached out to her and offered her a chair and a seat at the table.

"Don't you ever stay ta home?" asked Ma with a twinkle in her eye, as she looked up from scrubbing the dishes and wiped her hands on a dishtowel. Truth be told, Ma was thrilled with a visit from Edna and missed having all her children under one roof as in days gone by. They always teased their young sister, because it had become something of a family joke that Edna liked to "tear up the road" with her Marmon, whenever the opportunity presented itself.

"Ma" (Esther) and "Pa" (Webster) Coons

"Look what she gave me this afternoon!" Edna pronounced merrily, opening the dishtowel to show the offending, decomposing potatoes. Crowding around the exhibit, they all knew instantly to whom Edna was referring, if not by name, and the group dissolved into laughter. Ma poked at the spuds, and then dramatically pinched her nose shut with thumb and forefingers.

"Gosh," said her brother Stanley, sauntering into the kitchen, summing up the situation in his inimitable style. "That Carrie's crazy in the head."

Recipe for "Lemon Pie Without Cooking"

The juice of one lemon and the rind
1 cup of sugar
1 cup of milk
2 eggs

2 tablespoons of flour

salt

small pat of butter

Beat whites last and sir in with the rest ingredients

(Note: the ingredients would have been mixed together and turned into a pie shell already made, baked in a hot oven at about 400 degrees until filling appeared semi-solid and crust was browned, about 40 minutes)

Lemon Pie

2 cup of milk

1 cup of sugar

3 tablespoon cornstarch

¼ teaspoon salt

2 egg yolks

1 lemon (3 tablespoons juice and grated rind)

Scald milk, mix sugar, salt and cornstarch and pour on milk gradually. Cook in a double boiler until thick. Beat egg yolks and add to first mixture. Cook three minutes, stirring constantly. Remove from stove and add lemon juice and grated rind. Cool slightly and pour into baked crust.

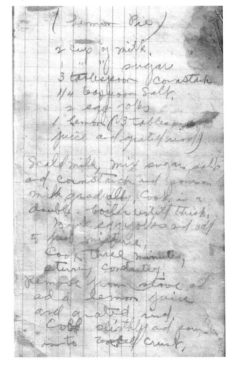

Edna's recipe for Lemon Pie

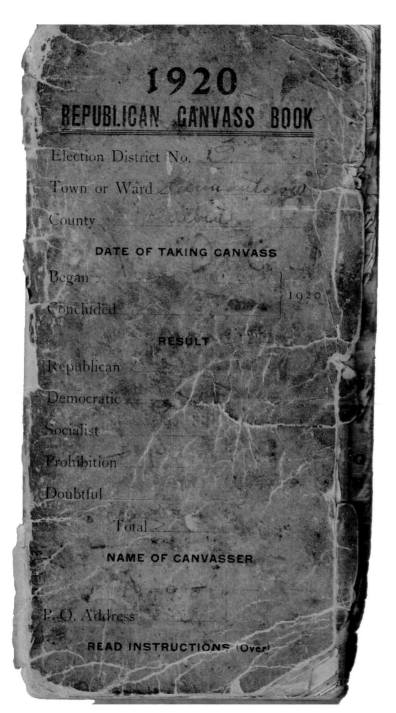

The Republican Canvass, which Edna used to record her recipes

The Coons family. Edna on left, in white, Blanche standing above her. "Web" in middle wearing hat, family friend Kate and Jennie on far right.

Picking pears in Germantown

Edna at 17

Edna in the mid-to-late 1920s

Chapter 7
A Little Girl's Fudge Cake

October, 1926

"I love pie, I love cake, For my sweetheart I will bake,'" warbled Edna as she made up lyrics to a strain of music she half-remembered from listening to a jazzy tune on her sister Blanche's wireless when she last visited Blanche's home. Even though using the electricity cost a lot, Blanche dearly loved to listen to her afternoon radio programs. It mystified Edna why Clarence, for all his modern thinking, simply would not have a radio in the house, since everybody knew it was the "latest thing". He was a man of contradictions, that Clarence. While he seemed fascinated by newfangled gadgets and machinery and how they worked, frustratingly, he maintained there was no need to have a radio. Surely he could justify one of the "contraptions", as he called them, as it would be especially handy in the mornings, for listening to the Farm Report and trying to figure out when the weather would augur well for planting or spraying the fruit trees and such.

Edna hummed the popular tune as she moved to the cupboard to get flour for the cake, kicking her foot to the side, then the other from time to time, as if she were doing the "Charleston" minus the hand-to-knee movements. She smiled to herself, thinking what someone might say if they popped into the kitchen, catching her unawares as she danced around. My, what high spirits she was in this afternoon! Reflexively, she patted her stomach, with the knowledge that another baby would join their little family in about five months. A third child! Would it be the boy Clarence so craved? One who would carry on the family name and farm?

In due time, what was to be would be revealed. But now it was time to get down to the here and now. Still, wouldn't it be swell to have a radio show to help pass the time as she worked? The people at those radio stations must have known that women would like to hear some instructive programs as they bustled about their homes and kitchens. That's probably why "The Betty Crocker School of the Air" started up in the past year, offering tips and recipes for the homemaker. Oh, that reminded her: she'd have to get Blanche to write down the receipt for "Radio Cocoanut Cake", which was scrumptious when they had tasted it at Ma and Pa's last Sunday. Blanche had written to the program producers for the recipe. Lately, with the demands of two little daughters and running the household plus helping out with the fruit farm, Edna scarcely had the time—or more importantly a pencil handy—to write down the ingredients when she visited her sister on days they listened together to the broadcast. She only had enough presence of mind to scribble down part of the recipe before it went into the "ether"! Blanche, by contrast, had become a veritable fount of recipes, especially now, as she was peddling her own farm-churned butter and sweet cream each week to the ladies in

the nearby city of Hudson, who not only paid her for her dairy offerings but also became confidantes of a sort, willingly exchanging current recipes, many of which bore the title "Hudson Women" in Blanche's burgeoning recipe book. If the weather was nice, they'd stand outside for a spell and discuss *sotto voce*, which woman who lived on the street "thought she was just *It*," (stuck-up) or who was a "Street Angel, House Devil" (pleasant to outsiders, but nasty to family).

Edna angled to visit Blanche when possible, so they could listen together, when one particular radio program, called "Housekeeper's Chat," was on the air. It had been launched by the US Department of Agriculture, Bureau of

Edna (in white hat) Clarence, holding Baby Doris, Esther front left, in Hudson

Home Economics, expressly to appeal to the farm wife, busy with home-making in her kitchen. The star of the show was "Aunt Sammy", which everyone understood to be "Uncle Sam's" wife. It was a neighborly chat for women who sometimes felt isolated in their farm kitchens across the country. Not only did it share wonderful recipes, but it also offered tidbits of chat and helpful hints about decorating a home, making clothing, buying appliances, comments on world affairs—well, they even threw in a joke or two to make the day go by faster! Edna smiled as she looked over to where little Doris slept. She was now a year and a half old, blissfully oblivious to the noise. Four-and-a-half year old Esther was playing quietly with her dolly, enjoying the warmth and camaraderie of the family kitchen. On impulse, Edna grabbed Esther's hands and gently brought the surprised child to her feet, continuing her made-up song, turning Esther around the kitchen in improvised steps, much to her eldest daughter's delight. Finally—finally! Esther seemed at peace with the idea of a

Esther and Doris

little sister. Edna couldn't blame the poor child for feeling usurped at the advent of another child in the family. Of course the Coons family had fomented the rebellion in Esther, and all for their own amusement. Even in the months before Doris was born, they had teased Esther—who, up to that point, had been the sole recipient of their undivided love and attention —saying, "I guess someone's nose is going to be out of joint: there's going to be a new baby!" Esther, keenly sensing that the unlimited love currently lavished upon her was possibly about to drain away, took the foolish talk to heart and became resentful. So, when Doris was born, and Esther was encouraged by Clarence to come take a look at her new sister, it was no surprise that emotions got the best of the poor child. At that moment, all the envy, all the fear that she was being replaced in the hearts of those she loved so dearly, welled up in poor three-year-old Esther's soul. Tears started to pool in her eyes, and before Edna knew what was happening, Esther's hand went up and she slapped baby Doris soundly on the face. There was a moment of shocked silence, and then the baby started to wail. Esther stood there, red-faced and fuming, but satisfied she'd made her feelings known. "Haw, haw, haw!" crowed Edna's brothers Stanley and Chauncey, slapping their legs in amusement. They always loved a good family controversy as long as it was at someone else's expense.

"Wasn't that pretty good?" they said, wiping their eyes with tears from laughing so hard. At that point, the whole family broke out in laughter, except for Edna who didn't find it funny in the least. She did not want her two girls to get off on such a bad footing. That's why, in the year since Doris' birth, Edna had taken great pains to have several talks with her eldest daughter, reinforcing that she was still loved and held a unique place in their hearts, even though a new sister had been welcomed into the fold. It appeared that Esther's coiled-up anger had finally relaxed and that she now accepted there was no turning back. Still, whenever she could, Edna took every opportunity to coddle her firstborn and make her feel special.

"She just wants somebody to make a time over her," said Ma, with the wisdom of a mother 14 times over. Edna remembered back when *she* was a young girl, how much fun it had been when you were made to feel special. Birthday parties were always an occasion growing up, even if it wasn't your own birthday. What a treat to dress up in your Sunday best on a day that wasn't Sunday, and attend parties bearing brightly wrapped gifts! It was a time for games and giggles and throwing off the boredom of the day-to-day routine. When she was young, the birthday girl's Ma would have made a layer cake frosted with fluffy icing, just for that occasion. Modern though the 1920s were, deep down, little girls hadn't changed, even in the 20th century. What captivated Edna as a child would captivate her daughters now. Edna flipped through the pages of her recipe book until she found the very one that would cause Esther to clap her hands and smile, especially since her birthday wasn't coming for three months: "A Little Girl's Fudge Cake".

Edna had snipped out the recipe from the pages of *"The Rural New Yorker"*. It was written by a young girl herself, one Miss Laura May Gleason, who claimed at age nine to be an old hand at making the cake with no adult help, as she had no less than three years' experience under her belt. Yes, it was just the thing! It was one of Esther's favorites.

Edna scanned the pantry shelves to see if she had sufficient supplies of cocoa. She scraped the remnants of the cocoa tin, and her assessment was that it would be just enough to make the filling and the icing. The other day, the newspaper said, cocoa and chocolate were becoming increasingly popular since Prohibition, with many Americans substituting their craving for liquor by folding themselves in the warm arms of legally obtained chocolate products. Who knew? Certainly this family of teetotalers loved their sweets for reasons unrelated to abstinence!

Rummaging for measuring spoons and pans, Edna felt a wave of gratitude for Ma and Pa and the fact that they absolutely doted on their first grandchild. They petted her and coddled her and gave Esther the kind of attention she needed and deserved. Heaven forbid that Carrie, living in the same house, would evince one little bit of interest in her own first grandchild. The woman acted as if the children didn't exist—or worse, wrinkled up her nose in distaste when they exhibited high spirits or got a little loud. "Hush now!" Edna warned, so the girls didn't end up upsetting their dour grandmother. Well, it wasn't Edna's fault if the girls came to think of Carrie as "That Mean Old Woman" beyond the door separating the two households. The words of Psalm 128 suddenly popped into Edna's head. *"And may you live to see your children's children"*. Edna dearly hoped that she would get to see her children not only grow and prosper, but down the line, provide her with grandchildren that she could hug and cuddle and spoil. Such a waste, that Carrie could not derive happiness from the delightful tiny tots who were her own flesh and blood and living under the same roof.

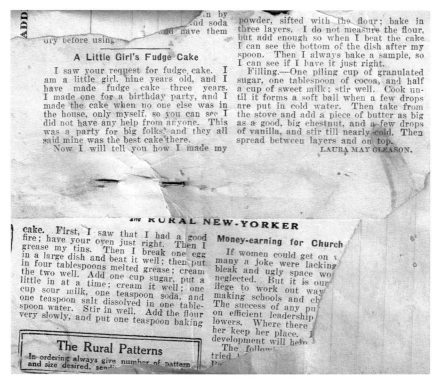

A little girl's fudge cake recipe, attached to the page by straight pin.

"A Little Girl's Fudge Cake" *

I saw your request for fudge cake. I am a little girl, nine years old, and have made fudge cake three years. I made one for a birthday party, and I made the cake when no one else was in the house, only myself, so you can see I did not have any help from anyone. This was a party for big folks, and they all said mine was the best cake there.

Now I will tell you how I made my cake. First, I saw that I had a good fire; have your oven just right. Then I grease my tins. Then I break one egg in a large dish and beat it well: then put in four tablespoons melted grease; cream the two well. Add one cup sugar, put a little in at a time; cream it well' one cup sour milk, one teaspoon soda, and one teaspoon salt dissolved in one tablespoon water. Stir in well. Add the flour very slowly, and put one

---

Believed to be from The Rural New Yorker, unknown date

teaspoon baking powder, sifted with the flour; bake in three layers. I do not measure the flour, but add enough so when I beat the cake I can see the bottom of the dish after my spoon. Then I always bake a sample, so I can see if I have it just right.

Filling.—One piling cup of granulated sugar, one tablespoon of cocoa, and half a cup of sweet milk; stir well. Cook until it forms a soft ball when a few drops are put in cold water. Then take from the stove and add a piece of butter as big as a good, big chestnut, and a few drops of vanilla, and stir till nearly cold. Then spread between layers and on top.

LAURA MAY GLEASON

Mrs. Tierney, September 1965

Listening to "Peter and the Wolf" on the stereo in our living room (it was a favorite Sunday routine of my Father's and, I think, his way of subtly introducing me to classical music and culture at a time when I was all about the Beatles and Pop Music), I thumbed through an ancient (to my childish mind) book that had been put in my hands as a gift. It wasn't my birthday—that was three months away. But the elderly lady who handed over this tome put it into my upturned, receiving palms with the same reverence that a priest would when distributing Communion wafers at church services. She bestowed it with gravity, saying, "I hope you enjoy this, Mary Beth."

I was used to older folks giving me gifts; as an only child I was doted on by my immediate family and a few other friends. On birthdays, I looked forward as much to my Great-Aunt Jennie's arrival on its own merits, as I did to the advent of presents and my favorite treat: traditional chocolate cake with thick, chocolate frosting. Aunt Jennie knew that I fostered a childish love of dancing along with the theme songs I heard on the television; she and my great-uncles got a big kick out of seeing me cut the rug when the first strains of those upbeat clanging banjos rang out with the "The Beverly Hillbillies" theme, among other TV favorites. For one birthday, Jennie had concocted a dream gift for a little girl; she had cut down my mother's long-packed-away, flowing pink evening gown from her youth, and reworked it into a pint-size version of childish sophistication. Jennie had expertly fashioned the pink tulle confection into a little girl's fantasy ball gown, cascading in layers all the way down to the floor. Instinctively, Jennie knew what kind of gift would engage the imagination of a child. I was transformed into a "star" the moment I stepped into the dress.

So, perhaps remembering the unbridled delight at receiving that particular gift, I unwrapped this rectangular parcel with somewhat less joy, although good manners dictated that I take pains to appear intrigued by its possible contents. Once the tissue paper was torn away, I found myself holding a timeworn volume of "Alice In Wonderland." Now, while I enjoyed old-fashioned books immensely, this still didn't pack the punch of an Etch-A-Sketch or a box of Colorforms. But, as politeness was called for, I thanked Mrs. Tierney (the gift-giver) profusely, and oohed and ahhed about how interesting the book looked, all the while secretly feeling a tad disappointed. Still, I had to admit as I examined it further, something intriguing cast its spell over me. This had a more tactile appeal than most older books, with its faded cream color cover, surrounded with embossed fleurs-de-lis and an oval in the center, highlighting pink carnations couched on a silver-foil background. I was certainly familiar with the classic tale of Alice falling down the rabbit hole, but had never read the story in its entirety. I had to admit, I was getting drawn into the experience simply by running my finger across the cover design, which looked like Victorian wallpaper. On the back inside cover, the inscription read, "To Esther from G.E., 1908". Maybe Mrs. Tierney had recently taken a stroll down memory lane via this beloved book, and wanted to impart the mysteries of the Looking Glass to a new, impressionable child? Moreover, who was the mysterious "G.E." it had originally come from?

I unfolded the wafer-thin onionskin paper Mrs. Tierney had tucked inside with its typewritten message. Perhaps she used onionskin—which back in the heyday of manual typewriters, allowed for easy correction of mistakes with the simple application of an eraser—because she was prone to mistakes when her fingers went flying across the keys, failing to keep up with the emergent thoughts from her head? The crisp paper was neatly quartered and rested inside the front cover with a message intended just for me—like Alice! It read:

"Dear Mary Beth:

When I was a little girl like you my mommie always had a birthday party for me. All the little girls would come in their stiff, starched, Sunday dresses with bright bows on top of their curls and braids and we had ice cream and cake and candy and nuts and prizes for pinning the tail on the donkey and MORE FUN. One year a little girl named Gladys Edwards who lived in the house where Mrs. Mickle lives brought me this book for a present. I liked it so much I kept it all through the years. More than half a century. And you are the first little girl I ever knew that I felt like giving it to. If you keep it as long as I did it will then be more than a hundred years old. That's pretty old!

It was signed "Mrs. Tierney" in a bold, unwavering hand.

From a child's eye view, Mrs. Tierney was a fascinating neighborhood character. I was initially intrigued by her because she was known around our small hamlet as "a writer", which lent an air of mystery and intrigue to her comings and goings. She wrote poetry, and perhaps had articles published in local newspapers but I'm not at all sure whether she ever made a substantial living as a writer or whether she ever wrote a real, published book. But in my eight-year-old estimation she surely qualified as a woman "of letters," and therefore, was to be keenly, quietly observed at all times. You see, at age eight, I had already made a stab at poetry (distinguished mainly because it rhymed, not because it was good), and harbored elaborate dreams of being a great poet or writer myself when I grew up. Of course I never told anyone, such was the zeal with which I guarded my secret. But at the appropriate adult time, I believed I would spring on the unsuspecting world my trenchant observations on everything and people would pay great attention and admire me for my deep thoughts.

None of this stealthy observation of the adults was evident and I was content to be "seen and not heard" in their company. Thankfully, Mrs. Tierney found an avid conversational partner in my Mother, who was far more skilled at communication than I. As an only child, I truly enjoyed being with adults—sometimes more than my peers—and while I spoke infrequently, I relished being able to *listen* to adult conversations about adult things, even the parts where they spoke in code, trading knowing looks over my head, convinced they were keeping their meaning from me. But I could translate the emotions and meaning behind the masked parlance. This was how Adult Women behaved when they got together. It was all part of my tutelage as a Female of the Species.

Mrs. Tierney always wore her silvery hair coiled in a bun on top of her head and had a whimsical mode of conveyance for a senior citizen, in that she drove a zippy little blue Corvair (this was about the time when its image was morphing from rather glamorous to possibly unsafe), which was a curiously sporty and youthful choice for a woman who at the time was midway into her sixties. Of course, back in the 1960s being *in your sixties* was hopelessly "square" two times over. This was the era when you were clearly labeled as over-the-hill once you were over 30. (Irony of ironies, those same Baby Boomers who, at that time, distrusted anyone over 30, are now redefining the definition of "seniors"). Mrs. Tierney lived in an old-fashioned house, high up on a cliff that overlooked the Hudson River. She loved cultivating flowers and occasionally would invite Mama, me (as I was my Mother's constant sidekick) and Olive, our elderly neighbor, for afternoon tea and cake. She had a large dog (possibly part St. Bernard, but mostly of indeterminate breed), who was exotically named "Faux-Pas," my first introduction to the unique French term. It seemed a highly chic moniker, equal to that of "Asta" the pup in the "Thin Man" movie series. The name was apt, as "Faux-Pas" was capable of getting into untold amounts of mischief at the drop of a hat.

I mused about Mrs. Tierney's little-girl companions of the early 20th century—she and her pal G.E., who turned out to be named "Gladys

Edwards". They were slightly younger but near-contemporaries of my grandmother Edna. I reveled in her description of their parties. I imagined them as incarnations of Alice herself, dressed in Sunday finery with outsized, festive bows in their hair. But what enticed me most was the idea of the birthday party, a Special Occasion where cakes and all manner of "sweetmeats" as the old books described them, were carefully laid out for the delectation of the invitees. All the best, starched linens were cast over the tabletops, smoothed down with a solicitous hand, and readied for company. Mad Hatter aside, the tea party tradition holds a very special place in a young girl's heart—again, it's the setting aside of the mundane tasks of the day, a chance to dress to the nines, behave like an adult, partake of cakes with pink icing, tasting ever so slightly of almond flavor, chilled glasses of lemonade and ...well, "MORE FUN," as

Mrs. Tierney put it. Humans dearly crave Special Occasions now and then in their lives, when we're on our best behavior, marking an event as something extraordinary.

Hard as it was for my eight-year-old self to imagine the elderly Mrs. Tierney as a child, I could remember the picture in a family photo album, of Grandma Edna, who would have been in her teens about the time of Mrs. Tierney's birthday parties. Grandma Edna was outfitted with that selfsame enormous bow peeking out from either side of her cranium, and she wore it with aplomb. She does not smile, which must have been unusual for her, given reports of her easy manner. She looks out at the photographer with gravity, under-

Grandma Edna at age 17

standing this photograph-taking was an important event and a record for posterity. Grandma Edna is wearing what might be described as a dark color "sailor suit", with painstakingly pin tucked sleeves, yoke front, trimmed with piping and covered buttons at the waist. No doubt Aunt Jennie, with her talent for sewing, had created this fetching frock. Grandma Edna wears black leather short boots with tiny bows on them. She looks young, beautiful and confidently serene, standing with her arms behind her, hands clasped, almost like a member of the military at ease. How different the customs were back then, when they didn't feel it necessary to smile or mug for the camera. Perhaps that's why Grandma Edna posed with such a serious mien; she knew that it would be weeks before they would see the results of the picture-taking and it was an expensive proposition. Her picture was marked "1911" and brought back echoes of the scene painted by Mrs. Tierney. Surely that was also a "Special Occasion"?

In contrast to their modest behavior, we carried emoting to extremes in the pre-digital pictures snapped in the mid-1960s. Everyone had an "Instamatic," a "Brownie," or a "Polaroid". Perhaps this ushered in the era of the more "candid" shot, revealing the true self perhaps, not the self you carefully crafted for others to see. In my teens, the Polaroid was a heralded innovation, allowing you to have the picture right then and there, giving you license to take another if the first one didn't suit you (depending on your budget for film and flash bulbs). With no siblings, I grew accustomed to having my picture taken, lots of times, a recording of that Special Occasion to put in the family album. Amusingly, at age two or three, I so hated the camera's flash, most shots show me with hands clapped over my eyes just as the picture is taken, shielding them for fear of the blinding light, which lingered in gray circles on my retinas for many minutes afterward. Yet I endured it, not for posterity's sake, but because I knew it would immediately be followed by my reward: chocolate cake with chocolate frosting. A Special Occasion indeed!

Radio Cake-Chocolate Cake*

  ½ cup shortening

  1 cup brown sugar

  1 cup white sugar

  2 eggs

  2/3 cup sour milk

  2 cups flour

  1 teaspoon baking powder

  ¼ teaspoon salt

  ½ cup chocolate

  1 teaspoon soda

  ¼ cup boiling water

  1 teaspoon vanilla

Put chocolate and boiling water together then put soda in

(Note: this would have been baked in a moderate oven –around 350 degrees)

Radio Cocoanut Cake

  1/3 cup butter

  1 cup sugar

  ½ cup milk

  1 cup cocoanut

  2 cups flour

  2 teaspoons baking powder

  1/3 teaspoon salt

  1 teaspoon vanilla

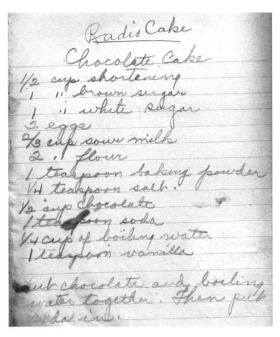

Blanche's Radio Chocolate Cake recipe

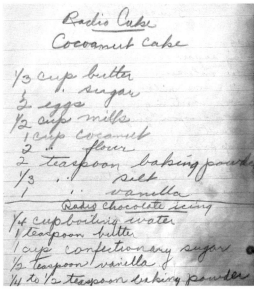

Blanche's Radio Cocoanut Cake recipe

---

*From Aunt Blanche's recipe book

Radio Chocolate Icing

¼ cup boiling water

1 teaspoon butter

1 cup confectionary sugar

½ teaspoon vanilla

¼ to ½ teaspoon baking powder

Cook for a few minutes. Good for cup cakes and sugar cookies

Radio Parker House Rolls

4 cups flour

4 teaspoons baking powder

3 tablespoons shortening

1 egg

1 tablespoon sugar

1 teaspoon salt

1 ½ to 2 cups of milk

Roll out, cut round, spread with butter and turn over, bake.

Chapter 8

Jessie's Green Beans

July, 1927

Clarence's red truck stirred up the dust as it careered around the corner of the driveway, its passengers hanging out the windows, draping themselves over the wood slats that surrounded the truck bed. The riders whooped and hollered and carried on, alerting Edna that her husband had picked up a load of what the townspeople called "bushwhackers" from up Lake Taghkanic way, so they could help him pick the ripening fruit crops that came in waves now that it was full-blown summer: first cherries, then peaches, then pears, then apples.

The "bushwhackers", as they were known, would have been called "hillbillies" in another part of the country. They were like a secret society—mountain people who lived apart from the civilized world, uneducated and often wild—and a law unto themselves. Some of them, like Edna, could also trace their ancestry back to the landing of the Palatines from Germany in the 1700s. They seemed not to want to settle into the small towns that sprang up along the Hudson, but started their own, remote compounds in the hills. One thing was certain, they didn't cotton to most laws or rules or regulations except the ones they made up for themselves. To a man, woman and child, this particular branch of the family was a pale, anemic-looking bunch, flaxen-haired and spindly limbed, looking as if they never regularly faced off with a plate of meat or any kind of nutrients that would wrap muscles around those scrawny bones. Nor did they appear to have had regular contact with bath water and soap. But to be fair, it was no wonder, thought Edna, as modern amenities, like indoor plumbing, which some took for granted these days, were completely foreign to these folks of the hills.

This particular clan's elder "statesman," a lanky fellow named Hort, had decided a few years back, to take up residence on the Yager property in one of the workmen's cottages. Hort was sensitive about his lack of education and should anyone question his mental capacities while he was trying to recollect a point, he would look aggrieved, scratch his head and utter his signature remark, "I know enough, I just can't remember it."

The truck screeched to a halt, as bodies leapt out, flinging themselves down to the ground in rapid succession. The women carried the strong, sturdy baskets they wove with their own hands, fashioning unique and dazzling patterns (which in later years would fetch high prices from collectors of this sought-after and rare folk art). Within minutes they had all cleared out, nearly as fast as they had arrived, and headed for the fields. Edna had to hand it to them, they were hard workers.

One grimy-faced little girl raised her hand and flashed a shy, crooked smile at Edna. Edna waved back, but by then the child's mother, exasperated, had yanked her into line with the others who were marching off to pick. Edna made a mental note to stuff a paper bag full of the extra crullers she had baked this morning and somehow get it into the hands of that little girl and the other children. At least it would give them some nourishment and a small treat for their hard labors.

Edna wiped perspiration off her brow as she bent down under the broiling sun to resume her task. She squinted her eyes, the better to focus on the string beans which seemed, chameleon-like, to be trying to blend in with their surroundings. From a vantage point underneath the speckled green leaves, she spotted an abundance of the long skinny pods, ready to be snapped off and either canned for winter or plucked right now, boiled up and set on the table for dinner. Goodness, this was a bumper crop this summer, with no signs of waning. From the first small white blossoms that sprouted, it was clear they would be picking, and picking and picking under this blazing sun. Edna believed she had had enough exertions for now and stood up, cupping her hands to shade her eyes as she looked toward the sun. She could see that there was a "mackerel sky"*—a sure portent that rain was due in the near future.

---

*mackerel sky- striated pattern in clouds, resembling scales of a fish, considered a sign of future rain

Pulling her basket from the ground, Edna realized she never looked at beans without thinking of her sister Jessie and her delicious recipe for string beans. Its final touch was lighter than a heavy cream sauce but retained both the flavor and tang of the fresh vegetable with just a little enhancement. Even though she was feeling a bit light-headed with the heat, Edna could almost taste the beans now, and would surely be happy once inside her cooler kitchen, that she had gone to all this trouble to harvest them.

Jessie's Green Beans

Trim a pound of green beans and when salted water boils, throw them in for several minutes to taste. Drain the beans, but then put them back in the original pan on low heat. Pour a small amount of milk to come halfway up the beans and add a pat of butter, salt and lots of pepper. Gently reheat until milk and butter meld together and warm to the temperature of the beans. Serve.

Edna felt protective whenever she thought of her sister Jessie—a silly, simpering dumpling of a woman, soft and round, not too good-looking, with doughy features and a general aura of being in a muddle. Jessie was considered to be a "trial" by the rest of the family, but surprisingly, she was often beloved by those outside the circle of her own relatives. Jessie was what they termed "a little slow". She couldn't absorb the complexities of life, or of living outside the comforting confines of her hometown. The women of the Coons family rarely took trips to New York City, but on occasions that they did, at least one of them would have to keep an eye out for Jessie, due to her failure to understand that fast-paced city streets made for difficult navigation. Jessie could easily be confounded by crossing a major thoroughfare, like teeming Fifth Avenue. On one trip, the rest of the family charged ahead when the light allowed for pedestrian crossing, but Jessie got to the middle of the vast boulevard, only to stand mule-like and stock-still, bewildered as traffic whizzed by her and car horns blared their disapproval.

"Jessie, come on!" the relatives entreated from the other side of the street, to no avail. Finally, as if getting a balking cow to come back to the pasture, one of them ran back to the middle of the street, hooked her elbow under Jessie's and dragged her to safety, hissing, "Keep walking, keep walking!"

Sometimes, it was hard to discern whether Jessie stood her ground out of confusion or conviction. She nearly got herself banned from the railway line when coming north from a visit in Poughkeepsie one day, managing to amble, blissfully oblivious, onto exactly the wrong train, which was not scheduled to stop in Hudson, her destination. Of course, Jessie would not have asked the conductor or the ticket-master upon boarding, whether the train stopped in Hudson. When she realized the train was getting close to her intended stop, Jessie decided to plant her considerable avoirdupois at the exit car, wailing loudly that she needed to be let off.

"But Madam, we do not have a scheduled stop in Hudson," sputtered the red-faced conductor.

By Jennie's telling of the tale, Jessie continued to "snot and cry," causing the other riders to take notice, some of them offering a handkerchief as she dissolved into a tear-stained mess. The conductor, realizing he had been outmaneuvered, angrily turned on his heel to speed down the corridor to speak to the engineer. Within minutes, the train showed scant signs of slowing down, as they approached the Hudson station. It managed a slow crawl—not a stop—as the door opened, and the conductor summarily ejected Jessie by her arm, onto the hard platform below. She landed with a thud, still clutching her pocketbook for dear life, eyes blinking in disbelief.

"Owwwwww!" bawled Jessie, whose ankles, while sturdy, were ill-equipped to support this rough discharge from a moving conveyance. The other passengers gasped at what had just happened, but the train picked up speed and whistled away to its scheduled destinations, before any real protest could be lodged.

That was typical of Jessie, who remained blissfully unaware of her personal "limitations" which embarrassed her relatives yet, inexplicably, seemed to endear her to others in the community. While her family was embarrassed by her exploits, much to their astonishment, Jessie's company was valued by the most unexpected of social circles. She repeatedly mortified both parents and siblings by sidling up to the members of the elite, high-society Hudson Garden Club, whose constituents (for reasons no one could quite fathom) took a shine to her, and kept inviting her to their "dos". Among their leading lights were landed gentry like the Livingstons.

"What are you doing, going to these luncheons with high-toned people?" blurted an exasperated Jennie.

"I don't care! I like them, they invited me and I'm going!" pouted Jessie, who wasn't quite sure herself why her company was sought after, but was going to make darned sure that she stuck like glue to her newfound friends.

As far as personal presentation, Jessie was shapeless and nearly sightless, given her propensity for rolling out pie crusts and other baked goods, then affixing her floury fingers to the lenses of her glasses to remove them while examining the recipe more closely. Mopping perspiration off her brow in a summer-sweltery kitchen, the dough-smeared specs would be popped right back on her head with never so much as a quick swab clean, leaving Jessie to peer through globs of half-formed pastry in order to see the world around her. When nieces arrived for a visit they studiously avoided her, as at any minute, she might lunge toward the unsuspecting child, gather her up into her vast apron-covered bulk and plant a slobbery kiss on the little one's cheek. (She was, it must be admitted, the original "blunder-buss"!) Far from being grateful, the child felt as if she'd been subjected to a saliva shower; while knowing it was wrong to hurt Jessie's feelings, it took super-human strength to refrain from demonstrably wiping away the vestiges of the excessive smooch. The child realized polite behavior dictated they endure the agonizing, slow drips down their faces until the adults got distracted by conversation. Then, unable to bear it for one second longer, the kids dashed out of sight where they could hurriedly wipe off the dribbly but loving assault. Not surprisingly, the floors of Jessie's house were eternally kruntzy*. In her

---

*kruntzy – dirty, sticky, messy with debris

defense, perhaps she was unable to spy the dirt and mess through her vision- compromised glasses. It seems the state of the glasses pretty much belied the overall mental blur through which she conducted daily life.

Jessie and Harry

Yet, when circumstances called for it, Jessie could be surprisingly clever. Never was that more evident than when it came to landing her man. Secretly, Jessie had set her cap for Harry Lasher, a businessman in town of kind disposition, passable looks, good education and some means. But her strategy for stoking his ardor when they met at church or other community gatherings was unconventional, to say the least. Edna's brother Stanley explained it after the family came back from one such event.

"Well, whenever they were sitting together, Jessie would break up gas, *" reported Stanley, in his supremely matter-of-fact way. Apparently, Jessie established herself in a chair on the sidelines of an event and

---

*break up gas--belch

every time Harry was near, she would "break up gas", hoping it would draw his attention, spark a conversation, and that ultimately the solicitous Harry might feel sorry for her.

"And then she'd start to cry," Stanley finished, noting that the waterworks were the ultimate nail in poor Harry's coffin. While some women might lament an inopportune output of the human body's intestinal workings at a public event, Jessie played the hand she was dealt. Edna was mystified that what might ordinarily be off-putting—an unrestrained show of belching in public—could in fact, lead to romantic appeal. But the Siren call of Jessie's indigestion apparently fanned the flames of not only sympathy, but passion in Harry's heart. And then, there was another small matter...

One morning, Jennie found Jessie, retching into a bowl. This was happening far too frequently lately, and raised Jennie's suspicions. Jessie looked up from the bowl, watery-eyed, face pale and skin clammy.

"Are you in the family way?" demanded Ma, cutting to the heart of the matter.

"I dunno," blubbered Jessie, setting off the waterworks again.

"Look at the snoot* on her! That darn fool girl went and got herself in trouble!" thundered Ma. "I never thought I'd see the day when a daughter of mine would be so sinful!"

Pa was a bit more compassionate, saying "Well, Ma, you know she's a little childish. She didn't know what was happening." But as the realization of the enormity of the news sank in, Pa's demeanor changed from protective to angry. He pounded his fist on the kitchen table. "But Harry! Harry knew darn well what was going on!" he spluttered.

Everyone knew, when an unmarried woman from a respectable family was found to be pregnant, there was nothing for it but the men folk needed to pay a visit to the bachelor offender. Pa and "the boys" went to Harry straightaway and impressed upon him in no uncertain terms, that his bounden duty was to make an honest woman of Jessie by marrying her. Poor Harry, thought Edna. Harry was quite a catch for any woman

---

*snoot- face, pulling a face, pouting, crying

in the tiny town, let alone dense and dimwitted Jessie. What had he *seen* in her, whispered the church ladies? He was essentially a decent man, a man with a bright future ahead of him. One moment's indiscretion meant he would forever be yoked to a foolish and uneducated woman; no question, she was goodhearted and an excellent cook but she certainly was not his equal in any respect. Matters were somewhat complicated by the fact that Harry had already been "keeping company" with another woman in the town. Stanley, who had actually laid eyes on the "other woman", leveled his assessment of her character and person, dryly sharing, "Wull, the only thing you could really hold against her was, she had a mustache." Hmm. So, given that bit of crucial evidence, perhaps it was not so surprising that Harry chose the apparent lesser of two evils?

Harry did the honorable thing, telling Pa and "the boys" that he would do right by Jessie. Edna "stood up" with Jessie, who cried through the entire wedding ceremony—no doubt due to a mixture of emotions, morning sickness and the gravity of entering the bonds of holy wedlock. And yet, with the unique irony of Life, just weeks after their quiet marriage, Jessie lost the baby. She was never able to get pregnant again, so Harry and Jessie remained a childless couple till death they did part. Harry's folly had been paid for dearly, with a shotgun marriage that was followed by no offspring to bless hearth and home.

Pie crust (enough for one pie)
   1 ½ level cups sifted flour
   ½ cup of cold lard or substitute
   ½ teaspoonful of salt
   3 to 5 tablespoonfuls ice water

Another good pie crust
   1 cup of flour
   2 tablespoonsful of lard
   8 tablespoonsful of water

Josie's Chocolate Pie

  8 tablespoons of sugar

  4 tablespoons chocolate

  2 tablespoons cornstarch

  1 or to eggs

  1 pt. of water

Green Tomatoes Pie

  3 pints of green Tomatoes

  2 quarts of apples

  1 ½ cup of suet

  Juice and grated rind

  1 ½ cupful each of raisin and currants

  half cup of vinegar

  2 ½ cup of sugar or more if needed

  ½ tablespoon of salt

  cinnamon, clove, allspice and simmer three hours.

The Singular Pleasures of Piecrust, 1970

In our family, the woman who owned the house was the High Priestess of the Kitchen. Others might assist in her endeavors, fetching eggs, milk, butter, flour, but after that, they were well advised to stand back and quietly observe. Additional offerings (especially of the *burnt* kind) were not accepted.

Part of this was due to her age and experience, but much of the solitary nature of her travails can be put down to thrift. Aunt Jennie was loath to let my mother and aunts cook in her kitchen, for fear they would waste ingredients or over/undercook something which would necessitate throwing out the attempt, resulting in an utter waste of precious time, money and resources that were, as previously mentioned, "dear".

My mother was far more generous in the kitchen, and allowed me to mix up some box cakes here and there, to get the feel of the process. But when it came to a real, labor-intensive event like making a home-made pie crust, I was content to stand aside to observe the alchemy involved. One of my Sunday afternoon treats was to look on as my mother made our weekly pie for dinner. This was a special event, usually undertaken post-church, after we'd changed into casual clothes and had our lunch, and it was a unique time of togetherness.

Until I started making pies myself, in my own kitchen, I never realized how much I learned of the intricate maneuver, purely by osmosis, while observing her technique. It's hard to get an attention-divided teenager to pay any mind to such mundane activities (although I had no trouble taking part in the robust *consumption* of said pie), so Mama exhorted: "Now watch, so you remember this." So today, when I make pie, I go through the self-same motions, and I think about carrying on this tradition in my kitchen, as did previous generations—not only my mother but her mother and all the females in the family before that. There is something so satisfying, so basic about using your hands to create a pie from raw ingredients, that it's hard to imagine why more of us don't do it "from scratch". It is something of a ritual, and like most rituals, it is comforting in its completion. There is something inspiring, even confidence-building, in observing a seasoned practitioner's hands as they create. I hasten to share my conclusion that—despite having no concrete mathematical formula to prove this hypothesis— I believe you'll find the deliciousness of a pie is *directly* proportional to the amount of care taken in preparing it.

Like many good wives married in the early 1950s, Mama had a roster of wonderful pie recipes. Apple, coconut cream, lemon meringue, chocolate chiffon, were all in her repertoire and denoted Sunday as a special day in the week. I remember the way she carefully measured the flour and the Crisco, making the important point that it was crucial, if you wanted the much-vaunted, truly "short" crust, to add a little extra shortening over and above what was outlined in the recipe. Then she plopped the shortening into the waiting bowlful of combined flour and salt and used a knife to cut, cut, cut, the mixture, until it resembled tiny beige peas. At that point, it was time to dribble in tablespoonfuls of ice cold water, carefully incorporating the whole mass with a fork against the side of the bowl, where it cohered into a solid, pastry ball. A small dusting of flour was smoothed across the waiting wooden work board, which kept the pastry from sticking. On one side, the board bore concentric circles of dark black rings, having been "branded" when accidentally set down on top of searing hot electrical coils atop the stove range years before. That indelible tattoo, attested to kitchen disasters as well as triumphs, and gave the work board a kind of character.

My mother pulled out the wooden rolling pin from its drawer and dressed it with what looked like a thin, cream-color, ribbed tube sock. The sock was shimmied up to the midsection of the rolling pin and served a clever purpose, stopping the "short" crust from sticking to work surfaces and the pin, which might render it non-transferable to the pie dish. She brought the pin down squarely on top of the crust mixture and made two distinct criss-cross X impressions on the ball, which allowed her to evenly roll it out into a thin crust, bearing the tiny grooves of the ribbed stocking after each pass. When it had rolled out to an optimal circle shape, she got a knife, inserting it between board and crust, thrusting back and forth underneath enough times to separate sticky pastry from the surface. Once about a third of it had been separated, she put the pin on top and gently draped the loose crust over the top, repeating the knifing pattern and advancing the pin to the opposite side, until the crust wrapped neatly around the pin and could be lifted *en masse*, for deposit into the waiting pie pan, to be crimped by hand.

As I follow this procedure I can remember the oft-quoted homespun advice of her friend Jan who said: "Then you *fork it* just lots and lots," meaning it needed to be liberally pricked with the sharp tines of a fork. Poke, poke, poke as the tiny punctures pierced the crust, allowing it to crisp up golden-brown and keep the filling from weighing it down into a soggy stew. Next, she would tumble in whatever filling was at hand: chopped apples laced with cinnamon and sugar; sweet-tart rhubarb chunks, pink and green, and redolent of spring; or occasionally blueberries or cherries. On other Sundays she'd bake the crust solo, to be cooled for several hours and later filled with coconut cream or lemon topped with clouds of meringue, sugary-moist dewy drops clinging to its tanned, almost leathery peaks when it came to the table.

Making a pie from bare bones ingredients is so labor-intensive, it's a wonder any of us ever assemble one in our own kitchens, especially as they are readily available commercially. Some, who have never watched the ancient art of making a pie, wouldn't have the first notion how to do it themselves. Yet, while in many corners it has become a lost art, certain folks will always set great store by the gift of a home-baked pie. Really, is there anything that so transfers comfort right down to our very bones with every divine mouthful?

Winter, 1928

"I won't! I won't! I WON'T!!" Little Doris' brow furrowed and tears looked like they were poised behind the curtains waiting to burst onto center stage. The little girl started to yank off the knitted pale green skirt that Edna had just struggled to wriggle up her legs, and Edna trained one eye on the clock. Oh dear, they were going to be late!

What on earth had gotten into the child to make her so stubborn on this day of all days? Aunt Anna had spent a month, painstakingly knitting and crocheting this beautiful two-piece jacket and skirt for her middle daughter to wear, but Doris was having none of it.

Edna put her cheek on Doris' forehead to check for a temperature. Cool and dry, no sign of the cold the little girl had suffered a week ago. Last week, it was clear the child was feeling poosly*, so Edna had pampered her a bit, wrapping little Doris up in a thick blanket, hugging her close. Anything to stop the poor little thing from whimpering.

"Are you hungry?" she had asked at the time, smoothing Doris' hair back from her forehead.

"Um, hmmm," nodded Doris with a weak little smile. Edna lifted her from the bed and carried the tot downstairs to sit in her lap, in the kitchen, which by mid-morning was toasty and warm. Edna dosed her with restorative spoonfuls of chicken soup, noting that the soup went down pretty easily. Still, Edna had learned that children often fought the very remedies that might make them better. Ma had always sworn by these prescriptions for both children and adults:

---

poosly – unwell, peaked "tolerably, indifferently well" (Modern Philology)

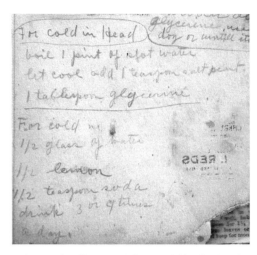

Coons family "cure" for a cold in the head

"For Cold in Head"

Boil 1 pint of water
Let cool add 1 teaspoon scant
1 tablespoon glycerine

or:
½ glass of water
½ lemon
½ teaspoon soda
Drink 3 or 4 times a day.

Edna remembered that when she was a little girl and had a cold, she greatly favored the remedy with lemon in it, and thought Doris might also find it more palatable. Sure enough, by the end of last week, the little girl had perked up considerably and the sniffles had flown the coop. So now, re-cuperation time was well over! And since she seemed in good health enough to pitch a fit at this inopportune moment, it crossed Edna's mind that the recalcitrant child had started "enjoying ill health" as some of the old folks might say, and the attention you received when others waited on you. Was she taking advantage of the power an illness confers, in that others will do whatever you ask, because they feel sorry for your condition?

"You *will,*" said Edna evenly, as she firmly readministered the offending skirt, sliding it up the child's legs, determined not to let her small daughter get the upper hand. "Spare the rod and spoil the child," she could hear Ma say, whenever the Coons children acted up. Just to be sure, Edna rubbed her fingers across the knitted wool, wondering if it was itchy and causing distress. No, that wasn't it. Aunt Anna had done an admirable job, with intricate patterns of knit-and-purl to fashion this lovely outfit. And frankly, there was no time to change.

"You're wearing it, and that's all there is to it!" Edna said, exasper-ated. What had made this child so youncy*?

---

*youncy-whiny, complaining

"Say!" said Clarence sternly as he entered the room. The tone of his voice, when his ire was raised, needed only one word to convey his utter displeasure. Upon hearing that Daddy was angry, the girls usually buckled under quickly, understanding his strong will would brook no uprisings. Doris immediately quieted down and merely sulked a bit, but allowed her arms to be wrangled into the jacket.

Clarence had returned from leaving baby Winnie with Jessie and Harry. The two of them doted on the nearly-one year old child and Edna gave them a chance to spend time with her as much as possible. She had some initial misgivings about leaving the baby with them and traveling as far away as Boston, even though it was just a two-day trip. But she tried whenever possible, to find ways to allow Jessie and Harry to spend time with their favorite little blue-eyed niece. Edna thought it was a shame that Harry and Jessie had never experienced the blessing of children. Although, after being embroiled in an event like this morning's contretemps, "blessing" was not the very first word that came to her mind when she thought of children! No matter. Now, the storm seemed to have blown over.

Today they were headed to Boston, which was a long trip. That's why they were starting out as soon as it was light. Edna and Clarence were taking Jennie to visit the famed Dr Elliot P. Joslin. Dr. Joslin was administering remarkable treatments to help those with "sugar". Back in Ma and Pa's time, and even well into the 1920s, hearing a doctor say you had diabetes was tantamount to signing your death certificate. People lost arms and legs and their eyesight. And died young. But since 1922, Dr. Joslin had made great strides treating diabetics with insulin shots. Jennie might be a good candidate for this new treatment, and her doctor was sending her 150 miles away from home to see if she was eligible for this new medicine. One good thing was, Jennie had a will of steel, and would surely follow the doctor's regimen to a "T": strict diet, exercise and insulin shots, even thought she would have to administer them to herself every single day of her life. Jennie was always the first to adopt something new, whether it was a recipe or crochet pattern, so no one worried that she wouldn't rise to the challenge, especially as it could save her life.

Edna read how Dr. Joslin's own mother was able to extend her life following his strict regimen and if it could work for Jennie, well that would be a wondrous thing!

With Doris settled, Edna took a minute to leaf through the pages of her cookbook to plan for baking when they got back home, probably day after tomorrow. She noticed how many of the receipts were constructed with the same building blocks: sugar, flour and fats. Absolutely the wrong foods for someone with Jennie's condition. How Jennie loved to cook and bake, and how difficult her new life would be now that she had to use all her reserves of willpower to stay away from foods that brought her blood sugar to dangerous levels. Considering the ingredients of all the family's favorite recipes, Edna felt it was no wonder, that Jennie had developed diabetes. For centuries, this had just been the way farm families ate! Outside of pickles, tomatoes and green beans, there were few vegetables on the table. Most of their family recipes were for "stick to your ribs" type fare, with piled-high potatoes, and gravy-slicked meats and thick slabs of bread and hefty hunks of pie or cake for dessert. Farmers needed something hearty to sustain them, before heading out to the fields and the back-breaking work of harvesting fruit. Yet the times were changing, even for those not fighting the battle of diabetes management. In the ladies' magazines, Edna was noticing more and more articles about women "reducing", including tips for keeping the extra pounds off and corsets constructed to slim the figure. Flappers, with their near-shapeless dresses, didn't leave room for curvy figures in fashionable circles, like the Gibson Girls of old!

Dear Jennie was the one who followed the latest fashions and could always figure out just how to achieve a particular look. Hands down, Jennie was the most clever, capable sibling in their family. There wasn't a thing she put her hand to that didn't come out perfectly. Sewing and handiwork were her special talents—in fact, had she come from a different background, she could well have become one of those women who were breaking new ground as dress designers in New York City these days. She'd seen Jennie toil over knife pleats in a skirt until they were sharp enough to cut butter!

Goodness knows it was getting harder and harder as the 1920s marched along, to keep up with the ever-changing styles, from hair bobs to scandalously short skirts. What was it that Edna had recently read about coming fashions?

"We are also beginning to see dresses having the pleated skirt of a contrasting material. We admit that the skirts are short; indeed, we see many young women whose skirts just reach the knee, and any tall woman with extra length of limb feels that most readymade dresses are assuming the proportions of Highland kilts. "*

girl and her elders. We are also beginning to see dresses having the pleated skirt of a contrasting material. We admit that the skirts are short; indeed, we see many young women whose skirts just reach the knee, and any tall woman with extra length of limb feels that most readymade dresses are assuming the proportions of Highland kilts. The hat worn by this figure was the popular broadbrimmed shape with no trimming except a ribbon band.

Fashion story on hemlines of the day, likely from "*The Rural New Yorker*".

Despite living her life out on the farm, Jennie studied the latest styles in the newspapers and occasionally, magazines; not wanting to spend the money to buy them, she waited for others to lend them when they were finished reading. Jennie transformed the bolts of cloth sister Jessie got from Harry's uncle who was a dry goods salesman in New York City, into clothing for all the women in the family. In addition to that, Jennie helped pick fruit, cooked and cleaned and maintained the family homestead for herself , Ma and Pa and the "boys", as her brothers Stanley and Chauncey, being bachelor farmers, were referred to. Yet Edna had heard that some of the less kind townspeople referred to Jennie as an "Old Maid" and "Spinster". Not that she deserved such censure; she had all the domestic talents needed and then some to make a perfect wife! She was smart and had a sense of fun, but only indulged in a little frivolity when the day's work was over, not before. She had a great sense of duty and purpose. Perhaps it was just the luck of the draw, but no boy in town had taken a shine to her, or gone so far as to propose to Jennie.

Edna remembered a defining moment in their youth when Jennie—brave girl that she was—had actually ice-skated across the width of the Hudson river, just to see if she could get to the other side! Surely at that time of year, the river was frozen enough to support her, but you never

*Believed to be from The Rural New Yorker- no known date

knew what warm spot might have melted a treacherous hole into the thick slab of ice, what ice-encased branch might catch a wayward skate blade, sending you down in a painful tumble to the unyielding, frozen surface or worse, down into the icy depths. Still, she made it across and then back under the eagle watch of all the kids in town, who had gone down to the shore to see. They blew on their hands and stomped their feet back and forth to fend off the chill, clapping and cheering as Jennie skated out, her figure getting smaller and smaller like the dot of a pin. It seemed like hours later that she reappeared, skimming the frozen surface with her skate blades, growing bigger and bigger, closer, and closer till she was back on the East shore of the Hudson, red-faced and breathless, a smile of triumph spreading into a grin across her face. Edna had run up to throw her arms around her; she was *that* scared something terrible might befall Jennie. So not only for her talents, but for her courageous spirit and can-do attitude—well, all that considered, it was Edna's opinion that Jennie should have been snapped up by one of the local farm boys years ago!

"She likes living home, and taking care of the boys," drawled Pa, who conveniently put Jennie's eligibility for marriage on the back-burner. It was probably because he liked having Jennie and the boys still living at

Left: Sister Jennie, in front seat with father
Right: Edna, in back on left with Jennie, in front left, dressed in men's clothing. Given several such photos, it appears that a pastime of the early 1900s was for women to dress in men's suits and have pictures taken.

home, and goodness knows they needed the help to run the fruit farm. He was unaware what secrets Jennie held in the recesses of her heart, what longings she had for a home and family of her own. Jennie kept it to herself, except for that one day last summer, when Edna and Jennie had found themselves picking cherries under the spreading canopy of leafy trees. Occasionally a breeze whisked through, keeping the stifling heat from overcoming them. They chatted to pass the time, speaking of a girl from church that had recently gotten engaged and was planning a spring wedding. Jennie, who seemed to have a touch of melancholy all day, suddenly grew silent and Edna looked over to see tears spilling down Jennie's cheeks. "Oh, dear heart, what is it?" Edna gasped, putting down the cherry basket to throw her arms around her sister. Jennie wouldn't look up but muttered bitterly, "It will *never* happen for me, *never*."

Jennie was not a bad looking girl, mused Edna. Her features were a little sharp, but nothing out of the ordinary. Maybe boys were intimidated by her capable nature. But more likely than not, Edna thought, Jennie had not married because she just wouldn't "settle". She had found no boy who set her heart to fluttering, like Edna had in her Clarence. In a small farm town, there were "slim pickings" sometimes. It was like that game of musical chairs. When the music stopped and everyone else had paired up, you were sometimes, through no fault of your own except plain bad luck, left standing alone.

Rueful that her sister had seen so little happiness in life, Edna remembered the recipe she had pulled out yesterday in her honor: "Jennie's Cherries Cake". It was a delicious, spicy cake, and even unfrosted, could be easily packed up for the long road trip ahead of them, nestled in napkins with egg salad sandwiches and a jar of pickles. They kept food cold by stowing it in the trunk of the car, exposing it to the cold winter temperatures. Edna counted the jars of put-up cherries still in the pantry— seven, eight, nine, ten of them in all. That would be plenty to last them till the next summer when fresh ones were available. It was impossible to underestimate the importance of cherries to the financial health of a fruit farm in upstate New York. Cherry season was eagerly anticipated, because once the cherries were "in," the farm could, at long last, start to breathe easier. Cherries were the first "cash crop" to be harvested for that season. Prior to that, they had to survive on what the apple crop, their biggest seller, had brought in through the past fall and early winter. So, a bumper crop of cherries was a very good sign that the growing season was not only underway, but in fact, expected to be lucrative.

Thankfully, on this frigid winter's morning, Edna rejoiced at her forethought in canning sour cherries back on that beastly hot July day, of the kind that made you just want to go lie down by a cool spring until the heat wave subsided. The canning process— the pitting, the boiling and sterilizing jars—well, it made the entire kitchen feel like a pressure cooker. But the fruits of their labors now benefited them, six months later, producing slabs of this tasty, clove-and-cinnamon flecked cherry cake that would fortify the intrepid travelers on their way to Boston, the Joslin Clinic and, she hoped, a new lease on life for Jennie. What a cruel blow, thought Edna, that Jennie, who dearly loved making and consuming sweet treats, would be denied them on all but very rare occasions. She would always, once she underwent treatment with Dr. Joslin, have to be vigilant about what she ate and how much she exercised. Yet, if any of the Coons children had the gumption and sheer will to take on such a regimen, it was Jennie.

Jennie Cherrie Cake *(from Aunt Blanche's recipe book)*
> *1 cup sugar*
> *½ cup butter*
> *2 tablespoons sweet cream*
> *3 eggs beat (separated, whites beat last)*
> *1 teaspoon cloves*
> *1 teaspoon nutmeg*
> *1 teaspoon cinnamon*
> *1 teaspoon vanilla*
> *1 teaspoon salt*
> *1 teaspoon soda in flour (mixed)*

1 ½ cup flour

1 cup cherries or any sour fruit

(Note: modern cooks could make this in a greased and floured 9 X 9" pan, with the option of adding 2 tablespoons of reserved cherry juice for extra flavor. Bake at 350 degrees or until a cake tester inserted in the center of the cake, is removed cleanly, about 25-30 minutes)

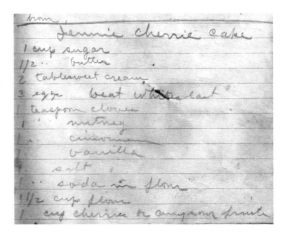

Recipe for Jennie's Cherry Cake

"Edna, did you see the paper? Did you see what the boys at GE in Schenectady were up to?" Clarence had returned to the kitchen with a bag packed for the trip. He was always full of enthusiasm for a journey to parts unknown and today, he was intrigued by what he had read in the morning newspaper.

"See Over Radio For the First Time," crowed the headline, reporting on the efforts of General Electric scientists in nearby Schenectady, who were able not only to transmit radio waves but an actual moving picture of a person—think of it!—for a few seconds on January 13. The report said that it was just a tiny, blurry image, but still—what doors did this unlock for future generations? Just as radio had changed their lives, this could have repercussions Edna couldn't even begin to imagine. What a world this was becoming! The societal changes of the 1920s were something Edna never could have dreamed of as she poised on the cusp of becoming a married woman, just eight years ago. Yet, while the modern world bustled past their doorsteps, the lives of farm wives were not so dissimilar from those of their own mothers and grandmothers. Edna thought of her three girls. They would grow up in a culture far more sophisticated than farm-bred Edna could even imagine. What would it hold for them? Failing—so far—to have borne a son to take over the family farm, Edna hoped that at least one of the girls might marry a boy who would be inclined to take over and continue the family fruit business. What would their lives be like in a world where you could see someone miles away, over the radio? Like a moving picture in your home! It beggared belief.

She was glad to turn back to something normal, something within the scope of her own experience that felt familiar. Time to pack up the sandwiches, pickles and cherry cake, and get on the road.

Cherries, June 2010

I'm standing at the kitchen sink on a steamy final Sunday in June, pitting fire-engine-red sour cherries that I've managed to pluck from an orchard in Columbia County, the homeland of my ancestors, just an hour's drive away. As I squeeze the rubbery orbs to get to the stone in the middle, I take care to reserve the dripping juice, so vital to the viscosity of the pie this is intended for. The tartness of the sour cherries stings my fingers and palms, which are already criss-crossed with scratches from harvesting the black caps in our yard that same morning.

The tedium of pitting the cherries causes my mind to wander and I think: did my Grandmother Edna do this at her own sink in the 1920s? Did she feel the same pressure I do, to get it gathered, get it cooked, get it preserved, frozen, secured away so that the family might have a tiny taste of Pure Summer in the vast wasteland that is a Northeastern Winter, six months hence?

My friend Sarah and I have a standing date, in late June or July, where we go to a Columbia County orchard and pay for the experience of picking sour cherries. This is one ritual that we never fail to observe, fitting it in for at least one hot morning that shows all the signs of ramping up to full-roasting temperatures by midday. We stand under the trees to catch a breeze, while we chat. We hoard cherries as if they are precious gems, stowing them in the freezer for a pie to be made in the dead of winter when the taste of sunshine and birds chirping, and the world blooming with ripeness, is just a dim memory. And we wait, for the promise of summer to come again.

Surely Grandma Edna and her contemporaries would have scoffed at the idea of "recreational" fruit picking, which is a common outing in this era of agri-tourism and "pick your own" (insert fruit here) endeavors. How she and her forebears would laugh at what they surely would see as our pretensions, our fetishization of food in the 21st century, with "artisanal" this and "locally-sourced" that. Fruit farming was a simple family occupation, the means by which they had eked out a living for two centuries. She would have been gob-smacked to see their orchard beset by zealous gaggles of vacationers paying to be dilettantes in the hard work of fruit-farming for an afternoon. And handing over real money to brag about their labors! What a mixed-up world, she would think. Still, in the 21st century, at our very human core, perhaps we all crave that closeness to the land, that symbiosis by which we tend the crops and then receive the soil's generosity as it yields back our daily food in abundance.

On the branch, the tiny translucent orbs are redder than rubies, brighter than the dark, sweet cherries on nearby trees. Your jaw starts to tingle as your brain delivers an oral memory of biting into one, feeling the squirt of puckery-flavor that's impossible to consume as is, but just begging for a dash of sugar and almond extract, not to tame the flavor, but rather to round out and enhance it.

And as we pit and prepare them for freezing, it occurs to me that there's a little bit of magic in preserving a piece of the season, putting it up on the shelf for safekeeping to be savored later. Like hearing "Frosty the Snowman" played on the radio when you're in the middle of a blistering hot July, pulling a treasure from the back of your freezer that was plucked in its prime and saved for use on the other side of the year—well, that is a form of Time-Travel in itself. Who wouldn't yearn on just one day in an upstate New York winter— whose temperatures have been unrelentingly set at 5 below zero, seemingly for weeks—to walk outside in shorts and flip-flops for just one January day and feel the strong rays of the sun? What if you could bottle a summer's Day and keep it up on a shelf, protected, like Grandma's preserves, to take out and slowly savor, like those priceless cherries we store in a secret cache for a cold, rainy day?

I had just such a "time-travel" experience with food in 1967 when we took the long overnight train ride to Elkhart, Indiana to visit my paternal grandmother. My Hoosier cousins pronounced her name "Grand-maw," as opposed to the "Gramma," dictated by my mother's side of the family. It would be a disservice to my maternal grandmother— the woman from whom I get half my name (Mary)—were I to fail to mention that while I never met my Grandma Edna, Grand-maw Mary offered me the full grandmotherly experience during our rare visits together. Grand-maw Wenger was a quiet, Mennonite woman, who never spoke without considering what she was about to utter—contemplating and choosing her words before opening her mouth to say something. It lent a kind of gravity when she spoke. You paid attention, even though her words were delivered softly. As a child, I felt obstreperous and shallow around my grandparents, who lived a life of deep faithfulness, modest means and quiet dignity.

Grand-maw had been a prairie schoolmarm, who at 30 years of age, married a man named John Wenger, who, I'm told, was, in his youth, referred to as "Black Jack" (for reasons still not completely clear to me although it did lend him an aura of intrigue). He was fond of telling tales of his early life as a Montana homesteader, waking up one morning to find snakes in his boots! Grand-maw apparently tamed him from that wild frontier existence, proving herself to be an industrious and dutiful wife, bearing him four boys over the span of ten years.

I loved to visit Grand-maw's house and examine her antique treadle sewing machine which sat prominently in her living room. She taught me the basics of quilting, how to hand-sew four patches of cloth with tiny stitches, to form the squares from which she fashioned the most impressive patterns. While my 1960s friends' grandmothers wore shirtwaist dresses—even "pedal pushers"—my Grand-maw dressed in serviceable, long dresses in fabrics with tiny prints, nothing garish, all outfits made by her own hand. Her hair was neither permed nor bobbed, but worn in a bun during the day; occasionally I would glimpse her in the morning through the bedroom door, brushing the considerable length of gray hair, then gathering it up, winding it into a snug coil and securing it with silvery fasteners, not the brown bobby pins I was more accustomed to. She wore a starched, white prayer cap when she went to church. The Mennonite services she attended were a revelation for me as a child; it was so unlike the standard Dutch Reformed service I was accustomed to. Theirs had no organ accompaniment or choir dressed in silken robes. At the appropriate moment, a man simply pulled out a pitch pipe and the congregants sang the hymn *a capella*.

After my Grandfather's death, my Grand-maw lived in the same tiny home where she had raised her sons, whose rooms were up in the attic under the eaves. That's where I also slept when I visited, which was a treat for a child, as access to the top floor was attained only by climbing up a narrow, steep set of stairs, almost like ascending to a secret tree-house. Her home, situated smack dab in the middle of flat land as far as the eye could see, had no television set, which, for a child of the 1960s who practically lived for TV and spent hours consuming it, was a deprivation beyond measure.

"You mean," I asked my mother, "we'll actually have to just sit around and *talk* all night?"

We tried to get out to the Midwest to see Grand-maw every few years but my father's work as a busy, small-town family physician did not always lend itself to vacation time. Yet, on this particular visit, my Grand-maw was keenly aware that she had not seen me that previous Christmas holiday, and had made advance preparations to make it up to me with a sweet surprise.

We always enjoyed a hearty Midwestern repast when visiting Grand-maw, and to this day, I can visualize it, laid out on her plain kitchen table: her "signature" meal was tangy, tomatoey, ground beef Sloppy Joes accompanied by thick slabs of satisfyingly chewy white bread, slathered with good, fresh butter. Sturdy slices from a round of orange-color Colby Cheese (which we never served at home, we were Cheddar people) was an unusual taste sensation for my palate. She rounded out the menu with an appropriate vegetable like green beans.

But this hazy summer afternoon with insects outside emitting a buzzing drone you could hear through the window screens, green grasses swaying, prairie corn shooting up to the sky, we entered the kitchen, and what to my wondering eyes should appear but a plate with dozens of frosted miniature reindeer! Here, in Grand-maw's kitchen was something magical: a cookie that was normally reserved only for the wintertime, defying the seasons by manifesting right there on her table! Knowing that I was partial to yuletide baking, she had pulled out her recipe for rolled-and-cut out sugar cookies in reindeer shapes, baked them until golden brown on the edges, and painted them on top with pristine vanilla icing. She had made them in the thick of a steamy-hot Indiana Summer, knowing that was when I would least expect such a treat! I ooohed with delight as I was offered one and chomped down on its antlers without reservation. Not only were they delicious—it was a supremely whimsical gesture from this serious, reserved lady, intended solely to please a small child. Eyes alight, I took another bite. Grand-maw gazed at me, with a sweet, small smile, happy, as maternal forebears have been down the centuries, to be able to delight and provide sustenance to a child in both body and spirit.

Chapter 10

Remember This about Fudge

October, 1929

Edna quickly brushed through her hair but something made her stop to check the mirror again. She pinned her hair atop her head, and rubbed her finger along a scar that ran alongside her throat. She almost wished she could leave her hair down to cover it, but a grown up mother of three did not leave the house with her hair hanging down like a child! Thankfully, the scar appeared to be healing nicely.

Earlier in the year, she had noticed with growing alarm, that a lump on the side of her throat just seemed to grow bigger and bigger and bigger. Eventually she could no longer ignore it and made an appointment with the doctor. "Goiter," he told her, "you'll have to go up to Albany to have it operated on." Thyroidectomy was what they called it. The doctors had cut out the growth and she had spent a few uncomfortable days in the hospital.

Oh, the bills that began pouring in! Poor Clarence, how would he ever be able to pay them? He had taken on more debt over the years, as he bought up more property to expand the fruit farm. His was one of the biggest among all the fruit farmers in Columbia County, stretching clear from one road to the next road over. How annoyed Edna was that her body had let her down so, and cost them a fortune in hospital bills when they could least afford it!

Thankfully, the hospital ordeal was over and her energy was back. Edna headed downstairs, pulled a pitcher from the icebox and poured a small glass of recently harvested grape juice. Mmmm, her appetite was coming back, and that tasted wonderfully refreshing. In late September, the last of the summery sun had shone down on Clarence's grape vineyard, and you could catch a whiff of the fruit, bluish-purple and pregnant, near ready to burst with their warm, earthy juices. Up atop the hill, where the grapes wound around the vines, Edna always stopped to turn around and admire a sight that never failed to astonish her with its beauty. There, high on the hill, you could look West across the Hudson River to see the panoramic view of the Catskill Mountains. Since she was a little girl, Edna's family talked about "seeing" Rip Van Winkle's profile in the mountain range. According to legend of Washington Irving, old Rip had unfurled his lanky frame near those far-off hills, and remained lying there, taking a snooze for 20 years. It was part of local lore that you could see the outline of his slumbering body in the bumpy mountain range.

"Look there," Edna would say to Esther and Doris, in the same way she had been told the story by her own Ma, tracing the mountain outline in the sky with her finger. "See his feet and then his knees? Travel north to his chest, to his chin, to his nose and then his brow. There's Old Rip, just sawing wood!" It was a fanciful story but one she loved to tell them. Doris and Esther peered intently, trying to grasp the whimsical vision of old Rip taking a nap in the majestic mountain range. They were delighted by the tale and asked her to tell the story over and over again, whenever she brought them along, up to the hillside here to cut the grapes. Grapes weren't picked; they had to be carefully snipped from their vines by an experienced hand. The harvest was good this year and had been turned into the delicious grape juice that accompanied their meals in the autumn. And many farmers donated their grape juice for Communion services at church. Of course, some people, even in these tee totaling times, surreptitiously turned grapes into wine in the privacy of their own homes. But Clarence would have a "cat fit" if that were ever tried on his property, with Prohibition being the law of the land!

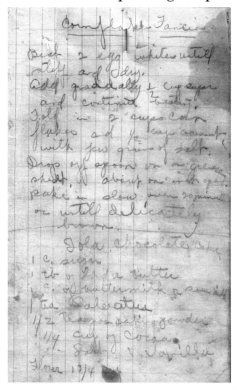

Edna's recipe for "Cornflake Fancies"

Returning to her kitchen, Edna took stock of the results of her day's baking. "Cornflake Fancies" were cooling nicely on the table. Such an easy recipe—just cornflakes, beaten up egg whites, sugar and cocoanut. It was a tasty treat and easy to store for a quick bite.

Thankfully, the "fancies" had come out all right, because the batch of fudge she had made was not a success. It sat there, in a woeful, grainy lump on the kitchen counter, with all the earmarks of a disaster.

Edna had followed the recipe dozens of times. And that was the problem. Instead of referring to it once more, she proceeded with making the fudge without looking at the directions, working from memory. She had been in a hurry, so she took a short-cut, stirring while the fudge was too hot, ruining the batch. Hadn't expert candy-makers like Ma told her to be careful, to the point where Edna had even written down the steps to be followed in her own recipe book as dictated by Ma?

The phone rang, jangling Edna's nerves because people rarely used the phone in the middle of the day unless it was an emergency or bad news. Her alarm turned out to be well founded.

"Come quick! Pa's bad, real bad!!" yelled her brother Chauncey urgently into the telephone.

"What happened?" Edna said, her heart lurching and her body starting to shake.

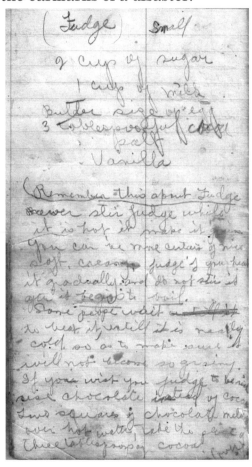

Instructions on proper fudge preparation *"Remember this about fudge. Never stir fudge while it is hot it makes it grain. You can be more certain of nice soft creamy fudge if you heat it gradually and do not stir it <u>after it</u> <u>begins to boil</u>...."*

"I don't know, he was in the barn and was fine one minute, then he just collapsed. Come quick!" Chauncey repeated, and abruptly hung up the telephone.

Edna gathered up her brood of girls and tiny Winnie gave out a cry, having just settled into a slumber. "What's wrong, Mama?" asked Esther with the eldest child's grasp of a dire situation.

Webster "Web" Coons, Edna's father.

"Your Grampa is sick, "Edna told them. "Get in the car, now!"

Edna's sense of dread mounted, as she shifted the Marmon into gear. Had Pa seemed a little tired lately? Now she thought on it, his color wasn't as ruddy and healthy as usual. Oh dear, what would await them, when they got there?

Pulling up to a stop at the house, Edna thought quickly. It was best to keep the girls from seeing what could be the sight of a loved one dying. They were far too impressionable to take in such a fearful sight. And they dearly loved their Grampa, who played the Victrola for them when they stayed overnight at the house. "Lazy Mary won't you get up?" he sang to the rafters each morning, as he awakened the girls for breakfast with musical accompaniment.

Edna's eye caught sight of the outside kitchen which was a separate structure just feet from the house. The family used it in the summer, when they wanted to keep the main kitchen free from the intense seasonal heat, combined with the day's cooking. Instantly, she knew that was a spot to stow the children at least for a few minutes until she sorted out what was transpiring inside the main house.

"Esther," Edna said, trying to keep her own voice from quavering, "You take Doris and Winnie and all three of you go to the outside kitchen. Now, I don't want you to come in the house until one of us comes to get you. Do you understand?" She said it with a firmness that could not be mistaken.

"Yes, Mama," Esther said, corralling her sisters.

Having packed the girls away, Edna dashed inside the house. They had Pa on the couch in the parlor and he looked a sight: ashen, weak and nearly unresponsive. They had unloosened his shirt a few buttons and were trying to pour a drop of whiskey (kept not for drinking, but for medicinal purposes like multiple bee stings or very grave situations like this one) down his throat, which he feebly pushed away with the remaining strength that he had. But even in the midst of the bustle of family trying to help him, Pa happened to look up and catch Edna's eye with such a strange look, it made time stop. It was one of recognition: of her arrival, of the gravity of what was occurring and something else. And it was at that moment, Edna knew. She just knew. This was the end.

"Oh, Pa," she rushed to his side and grabbed his hand, fighting back tears. He attempted a weak smile, and appeared comforted by having his wife and children around him. He already had the look of a man who had one foot on this earth, but the other in a place beyond.

"We called the Doctor," said Chauncey, with a choke in his throat. He turned away and brushed the rough sleeve of his work shirt across his eyes. No one said what they were all thinking: the doctor was not going to make it in time.

And then, Pa simply closed his eyes and was peacefully carried away from them.

Back row, left to right: "Ma" (Esther), Edna, "Pa" (Webster). Front row, left to right: Winnie, Esther, Doris

Ma started crying softly, and they all stood there silent, not knowing what to do or say. But their moment of grief was interrupted by an unearthly commotion, coming from the outside kitchen. The girls! She'd forgotten them in the midst of all that was happening!

Plunk, plunk plunk!! The discordant notes rang out from the old organ that had been disposed of years ago in the outside kitchen. Much to Edna's chagrin, it was clear the organ still worked, to deafening evidence. "Plunk, plunk plunk!!" How long had the girls been out there on their own? No doubt they had become bored with their surroundings and seized upon the first thing they could find to entertain themselves. They'd spotted the abandoned organ and started employing keys haphazardly, their little voices rising in happy disharmony, oblivious to the serious loss that had just transpired inside the main house. How could they have known?

Edna raced out to the kitchen. "Stop it, stop it this instant!" she barked. She so rarely chided the girls, they were shocked in place, with terrified faces, halted fingers poised in midair, now fearful of coming down on that next key. "Your Grandpa has just died! Have a little respect!" Edna said. The girls looked so stricken, the minute the words were out of her mouth, she instantly regretted being so sharp with them. "Oh, my little dears, you weren't to know," she said, gathering them all in her arms and hugging them so tightly, Doris complained. "Mama, I can't breathe!"

*****

Days later, the stock market crashed. People were jumping out of upper story windows—to their deaths— in their panic. Now Pa was gone, was the whole world going to pieces?

Looking at the gloomy headlines about the crash, Jennie said, "It would've killed Pa to see this happen, had he lived." "Web" Coons was fond of making a trip once a year to the floor of the New York Stock Market, to survey the bustle of business and share in the camaraderie that ownership of stocks in thriving American businesses conferred. Web owned stock in the Wabash Railway out of Indiana and Royal Dutch/ Shell Petroleum, the big oil company. It made him feel like he was part of the up-to-date business world, a more substantial man than just an outmoded farmer who knew nothing better of modern enterprise, than to till the fields, as his family had done for two centuries.

Why, Pa was fond of recounting that, one time at the Stock Market, he bumped into one of the august Livingstons, descendants of the great Lord of the Manor. Mr. Livingston graciously grabbed Pa's hand and shook it hard in fond greeting. They launched into a conversation about crops, like the gentlemen farmers they were, hailing from the same county, with the same arable concerns, forgetting that their social stations were miles and miles apart.

And yet, for all his admiration of American industry and commerce teeming here on Wall Street, Pa was still rooted in his true "stock and trade": the very land he tended, that had given his family comfort, sustenance and succor for generations. It put Edna in mind of that article Blanche had clipped out of *"The Rural New*

Web with horse and livestock on his farm

Yorker", which Pa sometimes quoted: *"When an old friend, who knows arithmetic and not another darn thing, comes along and asks to see your balance sheet, don't show it to him. Show him instead the new roof on the barn and what's under it. Show him the corn crib, the sleek stock and all that stuff in the cellar. Ask him if he ever tried eating stocks and bonds and bookkeeping entries for breakfast on a cold winter's morning. Then you can shut him up pretty effectively by telling him the farm is your home, and you are living on it and from it—not just cropping it...*

It was like Pa always said, after a particularly good harvest, reflecting on the bounty of his own good green earth (and perhaps, on less fortunate farmers), "Edna, you're rich— when you can eat." Dear Old Pa, he was

---

*Believed to be from The Rural New Yorker- no known date of publication

always right about such things. And now, the family was forced to go on with life, without his love and wise guidance.

As Edna straightened up from cutting vegetables over the sink, she winced from a sharp ache in her back. It had become a near-constant malady lately, right on the heels of the goiter. What *now*? Probably she'd been overdoing it, these past few weeks, just as Ma and Jennie and Jessie had, cooking and cleaning the house so things would be ready for the steady stream of mourners who came to pay their respects to Pa. No doubt it would go away if she could just get a few good night's rest. Is it possible she had a touch of the rheumatism, in her mid-thirties? She'd have to look up Blanche's remedy for that.

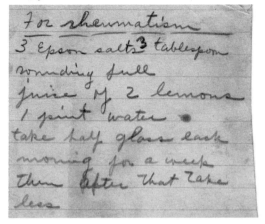

One of Blanche's remedies for rheumatism

For rheumatism

3 epsom salts 3 tablespoon rounding full

juice of 2 lemons

1 pint water

take half glass each morning for a week then after that take less

Another remedy from Blanche:

5 grains sodium Saleratus* for rheumatism"

Cornflake Fancies

Beat 2 egg whites until stiff and dry. Add gradually ½ cup sugar and continue beating. Fold in 2 cups corn flakes and ½ cup cocoanut with few grains of salt. Drop off spoon on a greased sheet, about one inch apart. Bake in slow oven 20 minutes or until delicately brown.

(Note: slow oven, about 250 to 300 degrees)

---

*Saleratus- baking soda

Fudge small

  2 cups sugar

  1 cup of milk

  Butter the size of an egg

  3 tablespoonful of cocoa

  salt

  vanilla

Remember This About Fudge *Never stir fudge while it is hot it makes it grain. You can be more certain of nice soft, creamy fudge if you heat it gradually and do not stir it after it begins to boil.*

Some people wait to beat it, until it is nearly cold so as to make sure it will not become so grainy. If you wish, your fudge to be rich use chocolate instead of cocoa. Two squares of chocolate melted over hot water, take the place of three tablespoons of cocoa. Do not add milk while the fudge is hot, the heat wilts the nuts and takes part of the flavor. Never add vanilla until after the fudge has been removed from the fire, as the flavor of the vanilla goes off in the steam.

Medium, November, 2010

"But I brought antlers!!" said my friend Mercedes, a bit disappointed in the unexpected turn of events.

I had been summoned, as had my three other pals, by our friend Charlotte, who had told us she was treating us to a Christmas-type pageant, an outdoor event where we would sing carols and popular songs and generally jump-start us into a holiday mood. When we converged at the pre-arranged spot where we were to pile into one car for the drive, it quickly became clear that the night's agenda did not include carols, Christmas decorations or antlers.

"You're taking us to the *Medium!*" pronounced Lisette, who had wised up more quickly than the remaining two of us, exactly what Charlotte was up to. It dawned on me that earlier in the year, Charlotte had enthused about a woman she'd met named Montana, who was a "medium".

Montana declared that she could put you in touch with dear departed relatives, that she could see them gathering around us even though we could not and that she had the unique ability to commune with them and their messages for us from beyond the grave.

Being a lifelong Christian, I was at first a bit alarmed at what seemed to be dabbling in the Dark Arts. I was unsure whether this kind of activity constituted necromancy, and downright godlessness. Or at the very least, foolishness. Were we being taken for a ride in more ways than one? Tempering that apprehension was the simultaneous acknowledgment that this experience was being offered to us as a gift, heartfelt and in good holiday cheer, like going to a magic show or a theater event. Noting Charlotte's genuine enthusiasm for this caper, I would have felt both ungracious at failing to receive it in the spirit in which it was offered, and—it must be admitted—I was already growing a tad curious as to what I might experience through this visit to "the medium." My father had died four years before, and I missed him dearly. Who knew—perhaps he might choose this opportunity to send a missive? On the other hand, knowing Daddy's stubborn constitution, he'd never do anything anyone prodded him to do, even in the afterlife. In life, it was a matter of personal pride that he would participate only on his own terms, so why wouldn't it be the same on the other side?

Misgivings set aside, we made the half hour drive, all the while chuckling at Charlotte's deviousness in tricking us into going along. We pulled up to a building with a distinctly church-like feel, and learned that indeed, it was once a rectory. Well, surely that wasn't so bad, was it? Montana, the medium, met us at the door. She was a blonde, plump, young woman, with an infant son and a sweet, disarming smile. She ushered us into a room that she said had been a small chapel in the house's previous life; in fact, this property was one of the few in a multitude she'd looked at when moving here, where she felt she and the spirits could comfortably co-exist. All the lights were on, in a typical living room setting: no séance frightfulness with candles and dark shadows. So, we sat, awaiting the show.

According to Montana, the dead are always around us. It didn't take long for my friends, who are sisters, to have their family gather behind them as they settled on a comfortable couch. As they discussed family matters, I was keen to learn the kinds of things the dead supposedly cared about. Some spoke of leaving a distinctive scent, or making bumping tapping noises that the living should pay attention to, since they were signs from the departed who were apparently, dead and kicking. I chided myself for the foolish thought: would Daddy show up? And what might he say? Seems these other folks had crowded in, and it was unlikely that I was going to have any visitors.

But after about 20 minutes with my friends and their ghostly relatives, Montana turned abruptly to me.

"I'm getting…your Grandmother on your Mom's side," she said, looking above my head as if the ghostly figures could be seen as easily as I saw my three companions in this room. Montana laughed and said, "She's very funny. I don't know if she means to be. She's not sure what to do and asks 'Am I doing this right?' She's just adorable."

This was not what I had expected at all! I had focused so strongly on some contact with my Dad from the other side, that I never imagined Grandma Edna, whom I had never met, would enter the picture. Nor did I think her aura would loom so large. I had not mentioned the acquisition of her recipe book to my friends, so I knew that Montana had not been "primed" by them ahead of time to make mention of Grandma. In fact, Charlotte had said, several times while in the room, "Maybe Mary Beth's father is out there."

But no, Grandma Edna was apparently most keen to communicate. "She's kind of blocking out everybody else, she's really big," shared Montana, as a chill ran down my spine. "She wants to make sure you know she's close and connecting with you. She is making a big deal about this. She's blocking out all other family."

What could this mean?

"She's so strong right now," said Montana, as if she was looking through us to those beyond the veil. "The first thing she's acknowledging is that she's messing with your TV," Montana reported. "She says there's a big reason for that and you'll 'get' why the TV's messed up." Montana had moved from another state recently so it was unlikely that she would know that I had spent 27 years in local television as a newscaster. And I had been off the local TV airwaves for nearly two years. Still, my reporter's skepticism kicked in. Was it possible that Montana had somehow "Googled" this information, or that Charlotte, in her zeal to convert us to believers, had shared information on my former career to authenticate the experience? The "comments" from Grandma Edna turned to my mother, her health, and her grief at the loss of my Dad after 55 years of marriage. Grandma Edna urged me to look beyond Mom's "game face" and get her to share that she was hurting.

Grandma Edna started stepping back, but before she did, Montana told me, "She adores you."

What was I to make of this? For a third time that year, my Grandmother Edna was thrust into my life, unexpectedly. Again, I had not shared any of my secret musings about Grandma Edna's life with Charlotte or my friends, so there was no advance preparation that could have steered Montana in that direction. We had gone there with the intent of connecting with my father, as losing him was foremost in my mind at the time. Yet, if Montana were to be believed (and I admit, that is a stretch), Grandma Edna was purportedly the first one "through". Could I believe this? And what did it all mean?

Call me fanciful, call me foolish. All I know is, I felt a warm glow driving home that night, just thinking that in some form, Grandma might—at least occasionally—be spending time alongside me.

Chapter 11

Saffron, Sage and Sorrel

August, 1930

SAFFRON SAGE AND SORREL

"Sorrel. Hardy perennial, used in the green state only. The leaves are sometimes cooked like spinach, and are occasionally used in soups and salads. The leaves, like rhubarb, contain much oxalic acid, beneficial to the system in spring. A pleasant drink is made by bruising the leaves and letting them stand in cold water, sweetening to taste; improved by burying the jug in cool earth for a day or more. Makes a cooling drink in fevers, and also acts as a diuretic and antiseptic in chronic urinary affections. A salve may be made by expressing the juice and evaporating it in the sun until of the proper consistency. Physicians esteem this highly in the treatment of cancer."

SAFFRON, SAGE AND SORREL 313

Saffron

A hardy annual, cultivated for its flowers, which are used fresh or dried in coloring soups, cakes, confectionery, icings, etc. Also used for dying cloth and Easter eggs. An infusion of the flowers is given to induce sweating. Also sometimes used to whiten the skin of infants.

Sage

A hardy perennial, more extensively used in seasoning than any other herb. May be grown from seeds or from division of the roots, the best plants resulting from the latter method. Pick the leaves and tender shoots for curing just as the plants are coming into flower. Does best on a very rich soil, with frequent cultivation. Indispensable for flavoring dressings, sausage and for seasoning in general. Sage tea is an excellent domestic remedy for worms, and is best made with an equal quantity of senna leaves, the senna acting as a cathartic to expel the dead worms. Use 1 tablesp. of each to 1 cup of water, and drink freely, until it acts as a cathartic. The hot infusion may be taken freely to induce perspiration.

Sorrel

Hardy perennial, used in the green state only. The leaves are sometimes cooked like spinach, and are occasionally used in soups and salads. The leaves, like rhubarb, contain much oxalic acid, beneficial to the system in spring. A pleasant drink is made by bruising the leaves and letting them stand in cold earth for a day or more. Makes a cooling drink in fevers, and also acts as a diuretic and antiseptic in chronic urinary affections. A salve may be made by expressing the juice and evaporating it in the sun until of the proper consistency. Physicians esteem this highly in the treatment of cancer.

Summer Savory

A hardy annual, cultivated for its stems, leaves and flowers, which are extensively used for flavoring, particularly in soups and dressings. Cut for curing when in flower. Winter savory differs from summer savory only in being a hardy perennial. Is used the same.

Thyme

A perennial, cultivated for its leaves and tops, which are used extensively for flavoring soups, sauces and dressings. Cut for winter use when in flower. An infusion of the leaves is efficacious in allaying nervous headache. May be drank freely.

Herbs believed to have medicinal properties-from Edna's recipe book.

Edna lifted her head from the bed pillows with difficulty, and took a tiny sip of the cup of sorrel tea Jennie had brought upstairs. This tea is stronger than I am, she thought ruefully. How many times had the women in her family made this particular concoction for all the many ailments people suffered in their community? Now, it was being prepared for Edna. To treat a disease for which there was no hope of recovery.

The lonesome wail of a passing New York Central Line train shot a haunting echo along the corridor of the Hudson River, and the sound made Edna sad. Hurtling along, it was no doubt filled with people going to destinations, to work, to family reunions, to shop in Albany. All those people with vibrant lives stood in stark contrast to a woman whose life force was ebbing.

Outside the window, the late summer sun had painted a swath across the wheat-color grass, leaving shadows of dark green on either side. Above it, there was "blue sky—enough to make a Dutchman a pair of pants,"—as folks in the Hudson River Valley often commented.

Up on the hill, at the spot where you stood to spy old Rip, still slumbering under his amethyst blanket across the river, the grapes would soon be ripening on the vines. If you thrust your nose near the bunches you would be rewarded with a sweet tang, intoxicating even in non-fermented state. Thank goodness this branch of the family had never become "topers"* like Byron and Fanny. There were enough problems in this lifetime.

Edna heard three pairs of small feet scuffing up the stairs, the first two accompanied by sounds of jostling and little-girl chatter, the final pair, slower and more deliberate, surely those of just-turned-three-year-old Winnie, who struggled to keep up with her big sisters, not wanting to be left out. Behind them, a fourth pair, adult feet, trod more wearily, accompanied by admonitions of "Hush! Don't excite your Mother!"

Edna knew in her heart there was something deeply wrong with her. She just couldn't get out of bed, had no energy, no ambition. Merely lifting up her head felt like a gargantuan task. She had been in Albany Hospital for test after test. What's the use, she thought. She could feel this terrifying "thing" eating away at her insides.

No one actually gave her disease a real name. They only spoke of it in half measures, and hushed tones. "She has ..." they would start to explain, trailing off so the listener could fill in the rest. As if not saying the full word somehow alleviated the crushing burden of the full weight of the diagnosis.

Cancer.

Late at night, when the rest of the house was asleep and he sat up with her, Clarence told Edna about the day Dr. Edwards pulled him aside and quietly confided that Edna had a terminal disease.

---

*toper- (pronounced "tow'-purr"---- drinker, alcoholic)

"All the world went black," Clarence told her. "I wandered around Hudson for an hour, stumbling around the streets. I couldn't think. I could barely take in that…that I was surely going to lose you. And with three little girls left behind…motherless…" His voice broke and he buried his face in his hands, inconsolable.

Dear Clarence. He had always turned a "can-do" face to the world, but since her diagnosis he had only looked bewildered and lost.

"What am I going to do without you?" he whispered a few nights ago, as he sat beside her bed, holding her hand. The thought of being a widower, with three small children, having to tend a large farm without Edna's help, now they were plunged deep into this major economic "depression" as some called it, just ate away at him inside.

"Ma!" said three little girls as they burst into the room, full of energy. The sight of Edna, pale and quiet, closing her eyes against the pain as she rested on her pillow, stopped them cold for a minute. She opened her eyes to look at her daughters: solemn Esther, at age eight, matured far too soon by the demands of her mother's illness. Esther had even started teaching herself to cook a little and could put together an admirable meal even early at the illness' onset, when Edna could hardly bear to stand at the kitchen counter for more than a few minutes, Oh, the back pain! She felt it again as she pulled herself up in the bed, the better to see her girls. The searing pain rarely left her. It just varied in intensity, depending on the day and the amount of morphine the doctor dispensed.

Next to Esther stood five-year-old Doris and little Winnie—all three dressed in their Sunday school outfits, posed as if for military review. "Oh you

Edna's three daughters, left to right: Winnie, Esther, Doris

look so pretty," murmured Edna proudly, reaching out her hand to touch them, smooth back their hair, to feel their sturdy healthiness. These little darlings, how could she leave them? As they climbed up on the bed to give their mother a hug, Jennie stood at the foot with a worried expression on her face. Thank goodness for Jennie, Edna thought. Where would she be without her help? Jennie made the girls' clothes and saw that they had their meals and were properly dressed for Sunday School when Edna simply didn't have the strength to even consider such necessities.

"Come on girls, that's enough," said Jennie after a few minutes of cuddling, rousting them off the bed where they had encircled their mother, "You have to go to church and your Mama has to rest now. You'll see her when you come back."

Edna could hear the commotion of the four of them as they left the house for church. Ma was going to stay behind from church and tend to her. A few weeks ago, it was decided that Edna would be moved to Ma's house, so she could be taken care of around the clock, by her mother and sisters. How good it felt to be in her childhood home! Still, Edna had no strength and no appetite no matter how much they tried to tempt her with morsels of her favorite foods. Occasionally she would try to take her mind off the pain by reciting from memory, the well-thumbed the recipes in her cookbook. Gramma Coons' Sugar Cookies—it had been so long since she'd made them. Now what were the ingredients for those? Oh yes, "1/2 cup shortening, 1 cup sugar, 2 eggs..."

Back when she was in the hospital—and it seemed like an eternity ago that she was there—Edna had enlisted the help of a kind nurse one night when she couldn't sleep because of the pain.

"Nurse, "whispered Edna, "May I have some paper and a pen to write with?" The nurse quickly obliged, and Edna pulled herself up in the bed, hurting all over, but managed to get into a sitting position. The hospital did not allow little children onto Edna's ward, so the girls could not visit her while she was in Albany. The only remedy for that was to send a letter to her darling girls. Winnie, at age three, would have little remembrance of her mother once she was gone, even if Jennie, Esther and to some extent, Doris, told her stories to keep her mother's memory alive. This was so *hard* for tiny children to understand! And this letter might, for all she knew, be her last missive to them. Surely Jennie would keep it, and encourage them to read it when she was gone? It was important to have something tangible that her daughters could hold in their hands that proved to them beyond a shadow of a doubt that their mother adored them. For all eternity. And that she would do anything, give anything, to stay with them, if only she could. Though she fought it with all her remaining strength, she could feel the slow ebb of life from her body. How strange, when she had so much to live for. She just had to send something to the girls to comfort them…afterward.

"I can't come home from the hospital just yet," wrote Edna, wincing as a shooting pain crackled through her back, "You girls be good and mind your Daddy. And no, Doris, it turns out I won't be bringing home a baby brother from the hospital, even though I know you asked for one. I love you all, very, very much. Never forget that! Your Mama. " Tears filled her eyes immediately, as remembered what Doris had told Jennie, when Edna first went to the hospital.

"She must be bringing home a little brother," said Doris with certainty. "That's why ladies go to the hospital. To get their babies!"

As so often happened on nights that seemed endlessly long, the words of Psalm 121 floated into Edna's mind and were a bit of comfort to her as she thought of the beauty of the Catskill Mountains. "I will lift up mine eyes unto the hills, from whence cometh my help. My help cometh from the Lord which made heaven and earth." Would help be coming for Edna? It seemed to her that if help were on the way, it would be to guide her to the next world, not this one.

*****

A week later and the family gathered around the bed now, a circle of sad faces looking down on her. They wanted to save her. As they hovered, Edna felt their frustration, grief, impotence. She wanted to soothe them, so she spoke quietly. "It's all right," she said. "I'm ready."

One by one, they came to say goodbye. Chauncey. Stanley. Ma. Blanche. Doris. Winnie. Esther. Abram. Clarence. And Carrie, who in what might have been the most charitable thing she had ever said, clutched Edna's hand briefly, then turned away from the bed and muttered hoarsely, "It should have been *me*."

And so, surrounded by those she loved, Edna closed her eyes for the last time.

Cherry Tree, May 2011

I am digging a big hole in the back yard, with the sun warming my head, my shoulders, my hands. It feels glorious, after a long winter of ice and snow and bitter cold, followed by a fits-and-starts spring, distinguished mostly by rain and chill. This is a day to savor. I thrust the shovel into the loamy cocoa-brown earth and pull up massive clods of soil.

I am planting a black sour cherry tree my friend Sarah has sent to me, an unexpected and welcomed gift. Its provenance is Columbia County, and the symbolism is not lost on me, not one iota. Here I am, committing to the soil of my own property, this tree that sprang to life from the same native ground of my grandmother, grandfather, great-aunts, great-uncles and countless antecedents who cultivated that land since 1709. By tendering it to the earth, I am making the very same offering they did in their lifetimes, as a gesture of hope and faith in better times ahead. As my cousin Cathy astutely observes of my fruit-cultivating-and-picking pursuits, "This is in our DNA!"

I get a good-sized hole in the ground and place the sturdy but small sapling into it. It's a good fit, so I dump a generous amount of water in the hole and check to see that the roots have plenty of room to spread and grow. Satisfied that they are well-situated, I scrape back into the crater, the large nuggets of soil and rocks and squiggly, fat earthworms, that I had upended from a Sunday-morning slumber just minutes before. I live about an hour north of Columbia County, where my fruit farming forebears measured out their days. My mother and aunts married men with different careers, who took them away from Columbia County; there was no male heir (as was the custom back then) to take up the family business of managing 102 acres of the Yager fruit farm.

Over recent decades, those old family farms have become second homes to well-heeled New York City folks. I'm glad to know the properties are still lived on, by modern families— perhaps with children who laugh and run and play on the property, as my mother and her sisters once did. Maybe a modern-day parent looks out the kitchen window while making their dinner, pondering the world, as my relatives once did? I wonder if the old fruit trees lie fallow, or do they struggle to produce yet another crop of the kind my family so greatly depended upon? As I tamp down the soil around the cherry tree, the symmetry of my actions continues to envelop me and feels right, somehow. I've been on a voyage of discovery— and when that wasn't absolutely possible, of *divining*—what the lives of my Grandmother and other forebears might have been like. Surely planting a tree, like establishing a homestead and having children, is an act of simple faith in the future—faith that this generation will come through relatively unscathed; faith that when you're tired and ready to put down the tools of your trade, you will pass on the earthbound legacy to those who come after; faith that "the Lord will provide," as Ma Coons said all those years ago. As I have no children, this is my way of passing on that legacy, that faith. Perhaps whoever buys our property, after my husband and I are gone, will enjoy the fruits of the black sour cherry tree, just planted, as we have enjoyed the black raspberries another owner planted, years before we took up occupancy. And so it goes.

During this odyssey of "finding Grandma," I have occasionally felt tears coming to my eyes, imagining how Edna felt, beginning with her excitement at the promise of an abundant married life ahead, when she first penned these recipes I have shared with you. Surely, like most brides, she had married at age 27 with hopes for a long, happy future. So, it is heart wrenching to think of the premature end of my Grandmother's vibrant life and personality at age 36. Sometimes, I have felt a longing for Edna, for that bond that might have been—but never was—between us. No doubt, had you asked her, she might have said that she had lived something of a "mundane" life, never straying far from her hometown, getting educated, married, working, giving birth and ultimately dying within the same few acres of land. But it was *her* life, and a unique one. Her reserves of strong spirit, good cheer, courage and bravery at facing an early demise, while shielding her girls from knowing the awful truth—were extraordinary. We never know how many sunny days we have ahead. So we try, to the best of our abilities, to enjoy what is set before us, sliced thick like a piece of Caroline's Spice Cake. It's up to us to devour each crumb. And having done so, to say, yes, I have lived, as well as I possibly could.

In my own way, I have found you, Grandma. Take my hand and walk with me a while longer.

The End

More Recipes From Grandma Edna

Author's Note: Unlike most of the recipes in the body of the book, some of which were updated for modern cooks, these recipes in their original state do not include temperatures and time for cooking and few suggestions as to the size of pan in which they might be prepared. Cooks in Grandma Edna's time had a sense of baking temperature and time born of many years of practice and trial and error. In the following recipes, "sweet" milk means whole milk, "sour" milk is buttermilk or milk with vinegar or lemon juice added. For those of you who have trouble reading the hand-written versions, I have written them up nearly exactly as Grandma Edna did, including grammar and spelling errors. I have added a capital "T" for tablespoon to distinguish it from the small "t" for teaspoon.

Consequently, readers who desire precise instructions might find the next section purely of historical interest! However, for the intrepid cooks and bakers who might want to try their hand at these recipes, I have included a few suggestions (see "Note" at end of most recipes and most of the comments in parentheses). Please read the recipe through before attempting it! I hasten to add that (unlike the updated recipes for Gramma Coons' Sugar Cookies, Aunt Jennie's Custard and Molasses Cakes as cited in the body of the book), I have not cooked/baked each and every one of these following recipes, so I wish you the best of luck in pursuing them!

CORN MEAL *(Jonny Cakes)*

1 cup of corn meal
1 cup of flour
1 cup of sweet milk
1 egg
3 teaspoon Baking Powder
1 Tablespoon butter
salt
1 Tablespoon sugar

(Note: mix above ingredients until just com-bined. Do not overmix. "Sweet" milk is regular whole milk. Place in greased, floured 8" X 8" pan at 400 degrees for about 15-20 minutes or until golden brown. Test for doneness by insert-ing a cake tester in the middle; if it comes out clean, the cornbread should be done.)

Edna's recipe for Cornmeal or "Jonny" cakes.

MERINGUE

Beat (remaining) two egg whites with ¼ cup confectionary sugar (until stiff peaks appear), spread over pie and brown.

CREAM FILLING

2 pt (pints) of milk or cream
½ cup of sugar
¼ cup flour
1 egg
1 teaspoonful of flavoring

Let milk come to a boil then add other ingredients and cook until thick. (Note: the stovetop burner should be kept at medium heat and the mixture should be constantly stirred to avoid burning.)

CREAM FILLING

1 large cup of milk, put on stove and let come to a boil.

Then put in a bowl:

1 egg

2 teaspoons of cornstarch

½ cup of sugar

Beat all together then add to the milk

(Note: the stovetop burner should be kept at medium heat and the mixture should be constantly stirred to avoid burning.)

CHOCOLATE PIE

2 Tablespoons of cocoa

1 cup sugar

3 Tablespoons of flour

1 or 2 cups of boiling water 2 eggs (separated, yolks and whites)

1 Tablespoon of butter

1 teaspoon of vanilla

Mix sugar and flour, stir in boiling water (as much as needed to make smooth). When smooth, add cocoa and mix thoroughly. Remove from stove, add yolks of eggs, beaten with one Tablespoon of water and butter.

Put it in a large pan of boiling water (double boiler), cover and cook ten minutes, stirring occasionally, cool and flavor with (vanilla). (Note: turn the pie filling into a pre-baked pie crust, chill in the refrigerator. Top with whipped cream or meringue if desired.)

MARSHMALLOW ICING

1 cup granulated sugar

½ pt. (pint) hot water

1 Tablespoon vinegar

Whites of 5 eggs

1 teaspoon vanilla

APPLE SAUCE CAKE

> 1 ½ cups of unsweetened apples (sic) sauce
>
> 1 ½ cup of sugar
>
> ½ cup shortening
>
> 2 teaspoons of soda dissolved in apple sauce
>
> 1 teaspoon cloves, 1 teaspoon cinnamon and
> a little nutmeg
>
> 2 ½ cup flour
>
> 1 cup of raisins

(Note: This appears to be enough batter to fit into a greased and floured 13"X 9" pan. It likely would be baked in a moderate oven—350 degrees—for around 30 minutes or until browned. The top should spring back when a finger is gently pressed at the center and a cake tester inserted into the center would come back with no crumbs clinging to it.)

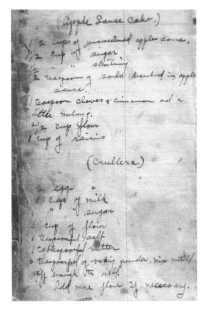

Edna's recipes for apple sauce cake and crullers

APPLES SAUCE CAKE (another)

> 1 cup of sugar
>
> ½ cup of shortening
>
> 1 cup apples (sic) sauce
>
> 1 teaspoon of soda
>
> 1 ¾ cup of flour
>
> cinnamon
>
> cloves
>
> nutmeg
>
> salt
>
> raisons
>
> nut meats
>
> citron

Bake 40 (Note: After the first five ingredients there is little precision in measurements. The cinnamon would likely have been 1 teaspoonful, with perhaps ½ teaspoon of cloves and nutmeg each, depending on the baker's tastes! It would seem it is supposed to bake about 40 minutes, probably in a moderate oven.)

MRS. STANLEY COONS'S (WHITE CAKE)

Into a measuring cup, put the whites of two eggs. Fill half with soft butter, (not melted). Then fill the cup with sweet milk. Sift 1 ½ cup flour, 1 cup of sugar, 2 level teaspoonful of baking powder (Sift all together three times). Now put into mixing bowl, add the contents of the cup, salt and flavoring. Bake in a moderate oven.

(Note: Flavoring could be vanilla, lemon, almond or another extract. This could be baked in a 9"X 9" pan, floured and greased before pouring in the batter. A moderate oven would be about 350 degrees. Baking time should be around 20-30 minutes, when cake appears golden, the center springs back to the touch and a tester inserted into the center comes out without crumbs clinging to it.)

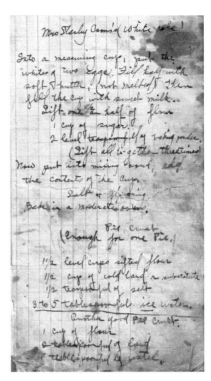

Recipe for Mrs. Stanley Coons'
White Cake

BANANA FRITTERS

    1 cup of flour add one (&) a half teaspoonful of Baking Powder

    1 beaten egg

    1 cup of milk and salt to taste

Beat well then add three or four chopped bananas. Fry in deep fat to a light brown.

ONE EGG CAKE

1 egg

1 large cup sugar

1 Tablespoon butter

1 ¼ cup milk

2 ½ cup flour

2 teaspoons of Baking powder

essence (flavoring, such as vanilla, lemon, almond extract)

and salt

Can be baked in loaf or layer cake.

(Note: the loaf pan should be of the larger, bread size. Alternatively, the batter could be placed in greased and floured round layer cake pans. Temperature would likely be moderate, around 350-375 degrees. Check at about 15-20 minutes for doneness.)

MEAT LOAF

2 lb. of steak and ½ lb. of suet

1 onion

½ cup sweet milk

1 cup of bread crumbs soak in

2 eggs

pepper and salt

3 teaspoons of salt

¼ teaspoon pepper

Bake one hour.

(Note: The amount of salt included is alarmingly high, so I would suggest cutting that back or omitting, given your dietary needs. Suet is unlikely to be used by the modern cook and is likely unnecessary given the two eggs included. It appears the bread crumbs are to be soaked in the 2 eggs.)

CLAM FRITTERS

2 doz. (dozen) clams

1 ½ cups of flour

1 teaspoon baking powder

2 beaten eggs

1 cup clam liquor

½ cup milk

Beat until smooth then stir in the chopped clams. Fry by dropped spoonfuls into hot fat.

ICE CREAM

6 cups of milk

4 eggs

½ cup sugar

2 cups of cream

2 Tablespoonful of vanilla.

Boil and freeze. (Note: modern cooks would make custard of this mixture then turn into a modern ice cream maker, following manufacturer's instructions.)

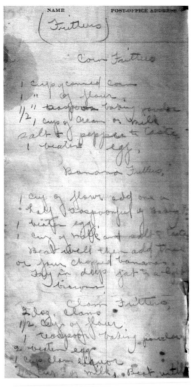

Edna's recipe for fritters

DATE PUDDING

1 cup dates (cut fine) 1 cup nuts

1 cup sugar

1 ½ cups flour

2 eggs

1 level spoon of soda ¼ cup milk.

Beat well and bake in slow (300-325 degrees) oven. Serve with sauce or whipped cream. This will keep for weeks. (Note: should be refrigerated)

PEACH DELICATE PUDDING

1 cup of milk (steaming hot)

1 cup sugar

1 Tablespoon flour

3 eggs (yolks and whites separated)

3 Tablespoon butter

Flavor with vanilla, add milk then cook, until thick, in double boiler. Beat whites of eggs and add sugar enough to sweeten. Bake pie crust first, add peaches sliced, then cream and meringue.

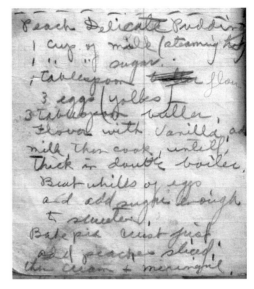

Recipe for Peach Delicate Pudding

(Note: this would have been cooked slowly on the top of the stove, stirring constantly until a custard formed, then turned into a pre-baked, cooled pie shell. Sliced peaches would have been placed on the cooled shell, topped with the custard and meringue.)

INEZ BOILED ICING

2 eggs whites beaten stiff

1 cup of sugar

5 Tablespoon of water

Boil until is (sic)strings, flavor.

(Note: the sugar and hot water would likely have been boiled up in a saucepan; "strings" apparently refers to the mixture "stringing" from a spoon when it is boiled clear. In a separate bowl, the egg whites (at room temperature) would have been beaten to stiff peaks, with the boiling sugar/water mix added slowly toward the end of the process. The whole mixture probably was placed atop a double-boiler and beaten continuously until the frosting surface appearance was shiny.)

EGGLESS, BUTTERLESS, MILKLESS

1 cup sugar

1 cup water

1 cup lard

1 cup raison (sic)

1 teaspoon of cinnamon

1 teaspoon cloves

1 teaspoon nutmeg

Boil five minutes, cool. Add 1 teaspoon of (baking) soda dissolved in a little hot water.

2 cups of flour

1 teaspoon of Baking powder

(Note: The first seven ingredients would have been boiled then left to cool. Once cooled, the baking soda/water mixture would be added and stirred up with flour and baking powder, turned into an appropriate cake pan and likely baked in a moderate oven, about 350 degrees, until browned and done.)

IOLA SHORTCAKE

1 egg

1 cup of milk

2 Tablespoon of sugar

3 teaspoon Baking Powder

2 Tablespoon of butter

2 ¾ cup flour

salt

(Note: these would likely have been similar to drop biscuits and served with fruit and whipped cream. The above ingredients would likely have been mixed into dough and dropped by spoonfuls onto a greased sheet, possibly at about 425 degrees for 10-12 minutes or until browned.)

FRENCH DRESSING

    1 cup vinegar

    1 cup milk

    Butter size of egg

    1 teaspoon mustard

    1 teaspoon flour

    salt

    sugar

    1 egg

(Note: butter would have been softened. All ingredients would have been mixed until they were of a smooth consistency and likely poured over vegetables.)

MAYONNAISE DRESSING

    Butter size of egg

    1 Tablespoon flour

    2 Tablespoons sugar

    salt

    1 teaspoon mustard

    3 eggs

    1 cup milk

    1 cup of diluted vinegar

SLICED CUCUMBER PICKLES

    6 qts. (quarts) cucumbers do not peel

    6 cup of vinegar

    1 teaspoon salt

    1 teaspoon ground mustard

    3 cups of sugar

    as much mixed spices as you think (about 3 teaspoons full).

SALAD'S *(sic)*

> Tuna fish salad
> 3 Tablespoons of thick mayonnaise
> 2 Tablespoons of vinegar
> chopped celery salt and pepper mixed well

Serve on lettuce leaf, California ripe olives and quartered tomato.

(Note: this recipe omitted the can of tuna but it is implied! The recipe itself is not remarkable, but it is interesting to note that cooks of the day had access to tuna in cans and California ripe olives.)

DRESSING FOR ALL KINDS OF FRUIT SALAD

> 1/3 of cup lemon juice
> 1/3 of cup pineapple juice
> 1/3 of cup sugar
> and the yolk of two eggs

Put lemon juice and pineapple, and sugar on stove to boil, just a little, and put in the eggs.

(Note: modern cooks would want to be sure the eggs were thoroughly cooked in this mixture.)

RED "DEVILS FOOD" CAKE

Cream together ½ cup Butter with 2 cups sugar add 2 eggs. 1 cup sour milk 1 heaping teaspoon saleratus (baking soda) dissolve in hot water.

2/3 cup of cocoa dissolved in ½ cup boiling water. Mix in order given last of all add 2 ½ cups flour and teaspoon vanilla.

(Note: It is unclear if this was baked in one pan or cake layer pans. Most likely it was baked in a moderate oven, around 350 degrees.)

OATMEAL MUFFINS

   2/3 cup of oats
   1 cup of scalded milk
   3 Tablespoons syrup
   ½ Tablespoons salt
   2 Tablespoons melted fat
   1 egg (well beaten)
   1 ½ cups of flour
   4 Tablespoons baking powder

Add scalded milk to the rolled oats, let stand ten minutes. Add syrup, salt and melted fat, mix thoroughly. Stir in flour which has been sifted with Baking powder, add egg and drop in well greased muffin tins and bake.

(Note: likely the syrup was sweet, maybe molasses, honey, or maple syrup. Muffins could be turned into prepared tins and baked, likely at around 350 degrees for about 20 minutes or until browned and tops spring back when pressed lightly.)

CHOCOLATE PUDDING

   1 pint of milk
   ½ cup sugar
   2 Tablespoon of cornstarch
   2 Tablespoons of cocoa
   1 teaspoon of butter
   vanilla

(Note: the milk and butter would likely have been melted on low heat in a saucepan, with the dry ingredients mixed together and eventually stirred in until all were well combined. Once well mixed, the heat was probably raised on the stovetop to medium, with the cook stirring constantly until the mixture thickened. Once taken off the stove, and cooled slightly, vanilla would have been added.

BLANCHE'S CREAM CAKE

2 cups of sugar

3 ½ cups of flour

2 cups of sour cream

3 teaspoons Baking powder

½ teaspoon of soda

4 eggs

salt

flavoring

FUDGE CAKE

2 eggs

½ cup of butter

1 ½ cup of sugar

¼ cup of milk

2 cups flour

2 teaspoonful of baking powder

3 small Tablespoonful of cocoa dissolved in ½ cup of hot coffee

pinch of salt and vanilla

Let the coffee, which the cocoa is dissolved cool before putting in cake and put this in last.

(Note: this is the only "mocha" flavor recipe I found in Grandma Edna's book. Since the recipe is followed with a recipe for "Filling" on the same page, my guess is, this was baked in layer pans.)

FILLING

1 cup of sugar

4 Tablespoonful of water

1 Tablespoonful of cornstarch

1 teaspoonful of cream of tartar

1 white of an egg beaten stiff

Flavor to taste

Boil this to soft ball stage, when tested in cold water, Beat altogether in two stiff whites of an egg.

(Note: It appears the first four ingredients were to be boiled up together, to be tested by dropping a small bit into a cold glass of water, at the "soft ball" stage. The white of one egg was beaten up into a separate bowl and the first mixture was likely incorporated into the whites to create a filling to spread between the cake layers.

PENUCHE

4 cup of light brown sugar
butter size of an egg
1 and 1/3 cup of milk

Let that cook up and drop it in water until it forms a ball. Then add your nuts and vanilla and beat again.

(Note: Penuche is sort of a "blondie" version of chocolate fudge, made with brown sugar. "Ball" refers to "soft ball" stage when making candy, when it is dropped into a glass of cold water to test consistency.

Acknowledgements

I could not have written this book without the love, support, technical advice and gentle guidance of my dear husband Denis.

Others who have contributed immeasurably to this effort, giving their time, their memories, their pictures and their support:

To my Mother, my thanks for recounting the old tales and sharing your own memories in vivid detail, without which, this book might never have been written; to my Aunt Winnie and Cousin Cathy, my gratitude for sharing your family photos.

To Jessika, whose genius, supreme patience and guidance made my "vision" a reality.

To my friends and "cheering section", including Beth Cunningham, Stephanie Lloyd, Jennifer Lanne, Katie Camarro, John Emery, Lori Rassas, Shelley Murphy, Charlotte Potvin, Lisette Rief, Mercedes Gaudier, I am humbled by your talents and grateful for your encouragement and the fact that you believed in me and the tale I could tell.

About the Author

Mary Beth Wenger spent nearly three decades as a television journalist in Albany, NY and was twice nominated for a New York State Emmy Award for her feature reporting and on-camera work.

Even though she covered politicians and presidents, captains of industry and the occasional celebrity, the stories she loved to cover most were about people living so-called "ordinary" lives, who were quietly doing extraordinary things with those lives.

"Finding Grandma: A Sentimental Journey Through 1920s Columbia County Recipes" was a tale Mary Beth felt compelled to write, mixing family lore recounted by relatives over the years spiced with actual recipes discovered in Grandma Edna's book, flavored with fond memories of sitting in Great-Aunt Jennie's Germantown kitchen as a child.

Find out more at www.FINDINGGRANDMABOOK.com

More praise for
Finding Grandma

This seriously wonderful book is just chock full of heartwarming stories of a bygone era mixed with lively entries from the present, all wrapped around such recipes as A Little Girl's Fudge Cake, Toilet Soap and A Cold In the Head. There are words of wisdom that make as much sense today as they did in Grandma Edna's day. Curl up in your most comfortable chair because you won't be able to put this one down.

—Stephanie Lloyd, writer, antique dealer, furniture designer,

Who would ever believe that a dusty old collection of recipes that the author found in the basement could be the incentive to create such an interesting book! The characters are engaging & you are effortlessly drawn into the stories, making it difficult to put the book down.

—Beth Cunningham, artist and owner of Artifacts USA

Mary Beth picked a genre that so rightly fits with home & hearth. It is vibrant with rich color, flavor & texture. Isn't it so true that the family recipes were not only just about food! We are invited to go waltz with her back & forth through time. She masterfully portrays the very recipes we use for living. Her style is unique & refreshing, & I hope her writing does not end with this book!

—Paul Cunningham, artist

As a cook, foodie and lover of all things vintage...the word that best describes this book is "magical". For all who cherish family, food and who "get the connection" to family history are going to adore this wrought with love collection. A lifelong communicator, MB Wenger has done an amazing job in bringing a piece of her family's history into a wonderful compilation of food, fun and fancy! You can almost smell the fire of the wood stove burning! This book is a fabulous social history of cooking, life and a woman's work in the 1920s era, I can't wait to see others enjoy this book as much as I do.

—Katie Camarro, "Sundae's Best"